GANDHI

GANDHI

FIGHTER WITHOUT A SWORD

BY

JEANETTE EATON

Illustrated by Ralph Ray

New York 1950

WILLIAM MORROW & COMPANY

TO RUTH TRUE

The author wishes to express grateful acknowledgment to

Dr. Taraknath Das
Professor of Public Affairs
Institute of Public Affairs and Regional Studies
New York University, New York, N. Y., and
Lecturer in History and World Politics
Columbia University, New York, N. Y.

for reading and criticizing the manuscript.

GANDHI

CHAPTER I

ALTHOUGH DAWN WAS BREAKING, IT WAS STILL DARK IN the hall. An oil lamp hanging from the ceiling gleamed upon the slender white-clad figures of a youth and a girl. Both were watching the stone stairway.

Softly the girl said, "Your brother is waiting for you on the veranda, Mohandas."

"Let him wait," the boy answered, grinning. "We have plenty of time to get to school. I must say good-by to my mother. She must be nearly finished with her prayers." He sighed. "Before I started at the high school, I used to help her put the jasmine wreaths on the images of Shiva and Krishna and Radha. Now I must snatch my breakfast and hurry."

At that instant a door opened at the head of the stairs.

A sweet, spicy breath of incense floated down. Lightly, as if borne by the fragrance, a slender woman came down the steps. Like the girl looking up at her, she was dressed in a sari, a garment consisting of yards and yards of fabric wound about the body and knotted at the shoulders. A wisp of the fine cotton stuff was flung over her head and framed a sweet, gentle face.

Laying a thin hand on the boy's arm, she said, "Good-by, Mohandas, my son, work well today."

"Good-by, Mother. Good-by, Kasturbai. May we all be given strength for our duties."

Kasturbai made an impertinent face at this solemn remark and said mischievously, "I suppose, my husband, my splendid duty is to make you a rice curry for luncheon."

"By all means," he chuckled. "Thanks to Mother, you are learning to be a very good wife to me."

With a polite bow to his mother and his little wife, Mohandas turned, strode the length of the tiled floor, pushed aside a curtain of matting covering the open doorway, and went out on the wide veranda.

A tall boy standing there turned to say impatiently, "You are slow at your farewells, my brother."

Without reply, Mohandas hurried down the brief path between hibiscus plants and out through the gate. As they walked along the dusty street, the two youths looked exactly alike, except for a difference in height. Both were dressed in long white shirts and full knee-length trousers. Their bare feet were thrust into sandals. Mohandas was very thin and short for his fifteen years. His step was light and quick and his lively dark eyes noted everything along the way.

A heavy cart drawn by two bullocks was creaking ahead of them. Now they were passing the town banker's big house of white brick set far back in a leafy garden. Between the lacy branches of pepper trees a servant could be seen shaking out rugs. At the corner of two streets a number of men and women were going up the steps of a temple. Under the portico they slipped off their sandals in order to enter the house of prayer humbly in bare feet.

In this way the day began in a small town in western India. Although it was many years ago, the majority of Indian people live in much the same way now. The climate is so warm that as much work as possible is done in the early hours. Therefore many schools open soon after daybreak and, like shops and offices, close in the heat of the day.

As he walked along with his brother, Mohandas remembered his young wife's parting remark and smiled. He and Kasturbai had been married for almost two years. Since he had no sister, he had never before known a girl. Nor had he so much as laid eyes on Kasturbai until he traveled with his family to her home at the time of their wedding.

That was a wonderful celebration. Days of feasting on delicious things! It made his mouth water to remember the sweetmeats and fruits and pastries. The wedding parade was a quarter of a mile long. True, the families were not rich enough to hire elephants, but drums beat and horses pranced. Grownups and children were dressed in the finest silks and linens and were weighed down with gold bracelets, necklaces, and rings. Most fun of all was to be the center of attention from all the older people.

For centuries and until just recently it was the custom

in India for boys and girls to be married at an early age. The parents arranged everything years before the wedding took place. After the ceremony the bride always went to live in her husband's home and was taught household arts by his mother. Consequently every house held several families sharing meals and everyday life. The father of the boys and young men was treated as the master of the house. But their mother, who taught her daughters-in-law, gave orders to the servants, helped prepare and serve the meals, and managed expenses, was the real power.

Mohandas, like all other Indian boys, took these things for granted. His eldest brother had been married for some time and was now in business. His second brother, who walked beside him to school, had been married at the same time as Mohandas and had shared in the festivities. Neither youth had expected to have anything to say about the girl he married. Mohandas, however, counted himself lucky that Kasturbai was pretty and spirited.

All at once his happy thoughts were interrupted by his brother's laughter. "Look out, little fool! You are walking right past the schoolhouse."

With a responsive grin Mohandas whirled about and crossed the courtyard to the low white building. As he pushed his way through the chattering crowds of dark-skinned boys in the halls, he made up his mind he would work hard that day. He wanted very much to make his father proud of him.

Karamchand Gandhi was his father's name. He was Prime Minister for the Indian ruler of a small state in western India. Although he loved all his sons, he was especially devoted to Mohandas, the youngest, and often said to him, "You must go on from the high school to study for a profession."

That afternoon, some time after he had returned from school, Mohandas said to his mother, "I am expecting my friend Krishna for tea. I suppose that is agreeable to you, Mother?"

They were on the veranda. Mrs. Gandhi was teaching Kasturbai how to embroider a blouse of fine linen to be worn under her sari. Mohandas had been working out problems in mathematics for the next day's class. But now he closed his book and fixed his eyes on his mother. She put down her work and looked at her son a moment in silence.

"You know, Mohandas," she said at last, "that your friends are always welcome in this house. But Krishna has had bad marks at school and has been punished for lying. Why do you invite such a boy here?"

Mohandas tossed back his head. "I am hoping to help him."

Kasturbai swung her head with its dark braids from side to side in a vigorous shake. "Krishna is not a good friend for you, my husband. You had best give him up."

A flash of black eyes showed how angry his wife's protest had made Mohandas. Disdaining to answer her, he said to his mother, "May we have tea served on the veranda? Krishna will be here shortly."

The sweet face of the older woman had turned grave. Presently she arose, beckoned to Kasturbai, and went inside the house.

When the two women returned, the guest had arrived

and was seated cross-legged on one of the thick mats scattered about the veranda. Polite greetings were exchanged. Then a servant in a white coat brought a tray which he placed on a low table. Kasturbai and Mrs. Gandhi served the boys with sugar for their cups of tea and passed small silver plates of curry puffs and spiced cakes. Bowing, they returned indoors.

As soon as the boys were alone, Krishna said, "I've been wanting to talk to you about something important. Like you I belong to a family of strict beliefs and was brought up never to eat meat. Yet I have been eating it for some time. Hah, my friend, don't look so shocked! Many good Hindus eat meat always. Lately even people of our strict group are doing so and I think you should eat meat, too."

Mohandas stared in amazement. "But why should I do such a thing? My parents would disapprove absolutely. How dare you suggest it?"

Krishna leaned forward eagerly. "We Indians must do something to gain strength. We have been conquered by the English. They despise and insult us and we accept it like weaklings. If we ate meat as they do, we might get enough courage to rise up against our masters. You and I could try eating meat in secret, and if it makes us strong we could tell others to follow our example."

What his friend said troubled Mohandas deeply. Could it be meat that made the English people so powerful? For days afterwards in his spare moments he went over all he knew of England's conquest of India. Only recently a friend of his father's from the eastern province of Bengal had sat with the family on the veranda. After accusing the British of taking vast riches from Bengal, he said to Karamchand Gandhi, "How long, my friend, shall we put up with these intruders? When shall we have something to say about our own government?"

As he thought back, Mohandas was even more startled by this question than when he heard it. He had not realized before how strange it was that men like his father and schoolteachers and lawyers at court had no chance to make or change laws.

One afternoon a few days later, the boy lay under a deodar tree behind the house, still puzzling over this question. Suddenly he whispered savagely, "Why should Westerners rule this land? They're upstarts!"

The word *upstarts* pleased him and set his mind happily at work. Every schoolboy knew that long before England was anything but a little island inhabited by wild tribes, India was a land of rich and glorious culture. Thousands of years of religion had given them spiritual training. Their art and their skills were the wonder of the world even before Rome was built. Indians had made beautiful fabrics, ornaments, and jewelry since the dawn of time, and from the ends of the earth visitors came to see the carvings in stone which decorated temples and palaces. How could the English think Indians inferior to themselves? Was it just because they didn't have modern guns to kill off invaders?

Mohandas closed his eyes to relive again the first time he ever saw these foreigners. He was only about seven years old. One day when he was walking with his father, a company of British soldiers came marching down the street. He stared at the tall figures in bright uniforms, at their sunburned faces and blond hair. "Who are those men?" he asked his father. Told that they were Englishmen from far away, he demanded, "Well, what are they doing here?"

Very clearly he remembered his father's patient voice explaining that for three hundred years Englishmen had been in India. They had landed first on the eastern coast to trade with the people of Bengal. When they found how rich the province was in gold jewelry, ornaments, and fine cloth, the strangers became greedy. They demanded that no one except Englishmen be allowed to trade with Bengal. Then they insisted on buying land for warehouses, wharfs, and offices. Troops of soldiers were sent by the British government to back up the traders' demands. Little by little traders and troops crept into the country. If the Indians tried to fight them off, the British always won. After two hundred years of fighting, scheming, and bargaining, the English became rulers of the entire country.

A feeling of shame stole over Mohandas as he recalled this conversation so clearly and remembered nothing of his own feeling about it. I was too young to care, I suppose, he thought.

Just then a gong sounded from the house. It was time to get ready for dinner. Mohandas sprang up eagerly and soon hurried to the veranda. Two servants had spread the cloth on the veranda floor. Presently his two brothers and his father came out and sat down cross-legged on flat cushions. Mrs. Gandhi followed with her three daughters-in-law. Little Kasturbai seated herself beside her husband.

Swiftly the two servants flew about to pass the food. A lentil soup called *dal* was served in small silver bowls. Thin

wheat cakes were passed with rice and curry and spiced cabbage. Each one served himself with his left hand and ate with the fingers of his right hand. No spoons or forks were used.

By the time the last course of spiced sweet cakes and fruit was served, Mohandas was ready to take up his theme again. "Father," said he, "will you tell me what power your chief, the ruler of the state, has under the English government?"

In surprise Karamchand Gandhi stared at his son. "The English governor of the district, appointed by Queen Victoria, is above my chief. That is so in every state and province. Even the Indian princes who rule their own states have to pay tribute to the British and obey their laws. Nevertheless, the prince of our state has much to say about affairs. He is admired by the men in the government."

Prime Minister Gandhi had an air of wishing to say no more and Mohandas dared not ask him another question. But the very next day he lingered after school to talk to the teacher of the English language. He was a highly educated Indian who had studied at Cambridge University in England. He spoke, read, and wrote English very well. He must know a great deal about the British, thought the boy.

"Do you think, sir," he asked, "that English rule is bad for our country?"

Thoughtfully the teacher gazed at the earnest face of his pupil. "There is some good in it, my lad. Many schools and universities have been started to train young men for civil service positions. Cable and telegraph lines connect us with the rest of the world. A number of railroads have been built and so have many good roads. This brings together people from different provinces who never knew one another before. Now, also, there are no more bloody wars between one prince and another. Indian troops commanded by British officers enforce peace."

Mohandas listened intently. These things were certainly good. But the teacher's face and voice suggested that much was wrong. An idea flashed into words. "In return for all that we have to pay big taxes and do everything the British want. Is that it?"

With a sad smile the teacher arose from his seat. "I am paid by the British government to teach you," he said. "So long as I receive my salary from them, I shall not speak against our mighty rulers."

Mohandas walked slowly down the hall. How did it happen that people all over the land accepted these conquerors? Indians must be weak. Perhaps Krishna was right. Maybe eating meat would make them strong. His mother would never believe this. Like all Hindus, she thought that animals were creatures of God and should not be killed. She also taught her sons that the person who ate no meat was helped to meditate about spiritual matters. Indeed, during the rainy season she took almost no food and then her face wore a look of unearthly beauty. Absorbed in his thoughts, Mohandas strolled slowly down the unpaved street under the tall palm trees. How often he had wished he could know as much about God as his mother. Nevertheless, it might be necessary for a man to make a different kind of sacrifice in order to gain strength of body and brain.

One afternoon he waited at the school door for Krishna. As soon as he saw him, Mohandas said breathlessly, "I have decided to try this business of eating meat. But I shall not tell my parents. We must do it in secret."

"Of course!" Krishna beamed with triumph. "I know meat will do you good in every way. You might even grow tall."

With a capering step along the dusty road, he began to chant the verse so popular among schoolboys:

> "Behold the mighty Englishman
> He rules the Indian small.
> Because, being a meat-eater,
> He is five cubits tall!"

Some days later Krishna arranged his friend's first experiment. With a package of goat's meat under his arm, he led Mohandas to a secluded spot near a small river. There he built a fire and roasted the meat on a spit. When it was brown, the two boys sat side by side on the bank and each picked up a chunk of warm meat. Mohandas choked on the first bite. He thought it was horrible. Only determination made him finish it. All the way home he felt ill.

Worst of all was the moment of facing his family. He was late to dinner. His father and brothers were just finishing their sweetmeats. Mrs. Gandhi signed to a servant to bring Mohandas his first course, but he said, "No, Mother. I do not feel well. I cannot eat."

Feeling her dark eyes upon him in grave question, knowing that his father would demand explanations the next moment, he murmured an apology and went to his room. A piercing pain filled his heart. He had deceived his parents and hurt the spirits of truth. He felt guilty and alone.

In spite of his suffering, however, Mohandas would not

give up his plan. Several times that year he ate meat with Krishna. Since his friend now took pains to serve it as one course of a good dinner, he began to like the taste of meat. But to deceive those he loved gave him a heartache. Moreover, one wrong seemed to lead to others. He smoked cigarettes on the sly, stole coppers left on the table for the servants, and at last pried out a piece of gold from his eldest brother's armlet and sold it. This he did to pay a debt for his second brother and made no gain for himself. Yet all these evil acts done in secret weighed him down with guilt.

At last he could bear it no longer. First he gave up eating meat. He no longer believed that was the way to grow strong. Next he wrote out a confession of all his other sins. The document closed with a signed vow to do evil no more. One afternoon, summoning all his will power, he took the paper to his father.

Karamchand Gandhi had been ill for some time. He was lying on a narrow cot and Kasturbai crouched beside it, fanning him. Opening his eyes at his son's entrance, he smiled happily. He did not notice that the youth was trembling from head to foot, nor did he see the imperious gesture with which Mohandas commanded Kasturbai to leave the room.

"Here is something for you to read, Father," said Mohandas in a choking voice. He watched the sick man struggle to a sitting position and spread out the paper. Sinking to the floor near the cot, the boy waited in silence.

What would his father say? In another moment, however, the question dissolved in the grief of watching his father's face as he read the confession. No punishment could hurt as much as the sight of slow tears rolling down the sunken cheeks. "Oh, Father, never again shall I do such things!"

Karamchand Gandhi did not glance at his weeping son. Slowly he tore up the papers and let them flutter to the floor. Then with a groan he sank back on the cot. At that instant footsteps sounded in the hall and he gestured to Mohandas to leave him.

For a time after he reached his own room the youth burned with remorse. Then, slowly, gratitude for the mercy shown him crept over him like a cooling wave. His father had said no word of reproach, because he really believed there would be no more deceit and wrongdoing. That night for the first time in months Mohandas felt at peace.

From then on his devotion to his father was unceasing. He rushed home from school to wait upon him. He loved those hours, especially when a reader versed in the sacred Hindu poems came to read aloud to the patient.

Month after month Mohandas watched his father grow weaker. Anxiety and sorrow filled the house. When at last death came, Mohandas felt as if he, too, were parting with life. But instead, life was rushing toward him with new and rich experience.

To begin with, as soon as he finished high school he took the examinations for college entrance. That he passed them all gratified the entire Gandhi family. Next he was placed in a small college near the west coast. Much as he liked his fellow students, he found the courses difficult and not too interesting, and when he returned home for vacation between terms he was in a discouraged mood.

Then came the great surprise! His eldest brother and a shrewd family adviser had decided that his best opportunity for the future was to become a lawyer. Therefore they were urging Mrs. Gandhi to send him to England to study.

England! Mohandas was thrilled with the idea. He would have a chance to see the world. "Mother," he pleaded, "you will agree to this plan, won't you? You'll let me go?"

Since her eldest son had generously offered to arrange funds for a three-year course, Mrs. Gandhi had no reason to hesitate. Mohandas won her consent at last by taking three solemn vows. He promised to eat no meat, drink no wine, and to be faithful to his marriage vows while he was away.

It was a painful wrench for Mohandas to part with his mother and Kasturbai and his little two-month-old son. But as he stood on the deck of the steamer edging slowly out of the great harbor of Bombay, he was excited as never in his life before. Deep in his heart he knew that an important chapter in his life was about to be written. The opening page bore the date September 4, 1887.

CHAPTER II

THE FIRST MORNING ON SHIPBOARD WAS LONG REMEM-
bered by Mohandas. Then and there he found out how
hard it was to become English. Friends had bought him a
black suit, white shirts, stiff collars, and neckties. Accus-
tomed as he was to loose cotton clothes, he found the outfit
most uncomfortable. The stiff collar pinched him. It was a
feat of skill to knot his tie properly. The short, tight coat
gave no protection compared to the ample folds of an
Indian cloak.

Nevertheless, his final glance in the mirror made him
feel quite proud of his appearance. With a light step and
light heart he went down the companionway and into the

dining saloon. The head steward waved him to a table. As he seated himself, another steward placed before him a steaming cup of black tea.

"What shall it be this morning, sir?" the steward asked cheerfully. "A kippered herring? Or bacon? Or perhaps a pair of broiled kidneys?"

Here it was—the assault of the English menu with its many meat and fish dishes! No Britisher would understand his vow never to touch such food. "Thank you, none of those things, steward. Bread and butter is all I need with this tea."

The steward departed to fill the order. Mohandas looked around the dining room. Since it was early in the morning, only a few people were down. All of them were devoting themselves silently to the business of eating. In surprise, the Indian youth watched the play of knives, forks, and spoons. Used as he was to the Indian custom of conveying food to the mouth with one's scrubbed fingers, it was all very strange to him. Nervously he took up a knife to spread his thick slab of bread with butter and marmalade.

Then he gulped down his tea and hurried up on deck. For half an hour he paced back and forth to the drumming of one question in his mind. How could he cope with this unfamiliar world?

At the end of his fifth journey around the deck he had made up his mind never to enter the dining saloon again. The sweets and fruits he had brought aboard with him were enough. Meager as was this fare, it sustained him through the long voyage. Dreamily he watched the Arabian Sea give way to the Red Sea and that sea to the Mediterranean.

Could it be that at last the dream was ended—that the ship was heading into the British Channel?

Mohandas had made one friend on the voyage. This was the distinguished titled Indian who shared his cabin. Unfortunately, he did not consult his friend before he chose the clothes he should wear for the landing in England. He was quite unprepared for his friend's greeting as he came up on deck to see the white cliffs of Dover.

"Oh, my dear young Gandhi!" cried his compatriot. "Why are you dressed like this?"

The young man looked down at his immaculate white flannels. "But I thought, sir . . ." he stammered. "In Bombay I saw so many Englishmen playing tennis and they wore clothes like these. I only wanted . . . I was trying to do the right thing." He flashed an agonized look at the waiting passengers. "But I see now . . ."

One and all the Englishmen around him were dressed in dark clothes. Bowler hats were on their heads and overcoats were flung over arms. These men knew what to expect of a cloudy September day in England.

If only his trunk had not been taken from his cabin! Wretchedly he endured the hours that followed. In the custom house and at the railway station he was the butt of all eyes. Surprise and amusement centered on the slim, short figure in white flannels. When he could finally sink into the corner of a compartment in the train, he had but one wish left—to recapture the trunk that contained his black suit.

This bleak introduction to England was a foretaste of what was to come. It was hard to find suitable lodgings. He almost starved until he discovered a vegetarian restaurant where he could eat all he wished without breaking his vow. Lonely and homesick, he was under the continual strain of trying to master Western manners and customs.

Mohandas had been given many letters of introduction and at once met two notable Indians who were old residents in London. Through them he met a youthful compatriot who became his friend and guide. The only disagreement between them was over the question of diet.

The first time they dined together, the young man listened to Gandhi's order in angry amazement. "What?" he cried. "You're not eating meat? Oh, this is too bad! England has committed many crimes, but she has one shining virtue, her roast beef!"

The protest was repeated whenever the two had dinner. In vain. Mohandas refused to break his vow. But in every other way he tried to show his friend that he meant to be as British as possible. He engaged a suite of rooms at a good address, bought fashionable clothes, took dancing lessons, and tried his hand at the violin. It took many weeks to convince him that he could master neither the waltz nor the violin and that he was gaining nothing by spending far more money than he could afford.

One afternoon he sought out his friend. His smile was pleading but his tone was firm. "I have changed my way of life. All this foolishness is at an end. I am living in one room and cooking my own breakfast. Now I shall give everything to study."

This vow was hard to keep. For between him and his textbooks the faces of his mother and Kasturbai and the baby kept looking wistfully at him. It took all his will power to crush down his longing to be with them again.

Mohandas wished he had the time and money to take a full university course before studying law. But at least he proved that he was capable of doing so. He passed the difficult examination for entrance at London University. It took him two years to do so, for at first he flunked the Latin test. But he persisted and, as he did so, grew to enjoy Latin. Meanwhile, he began the study of law.

After he had interviewed the proper authorities and registered as a student, he hurried to see his friend. With an amused grin he said, "Really I am amazed at the way law training is given here. The whole system is as lax as a loose rope."

"I've heard so," nodded his friend. "But some of the traditions are very picturesque. As for the Inns of Court, I think they are the most delightful things in London."

The Inns of Court are scattered groups of quaint old houses, halls, and buildings. Set around quiet grass courts in the oldest part of London near the Thames River, they are reached from noisy business streets by winding lanes, archways, and gates. In the old days students all lived in these inns and were in close touch with practicing lawyers and judges. In 1888, however, law students lived anywhere they pleased.

At that time in England it was easy to become a lawyer. Two types of law governed court decisions: Roman law, which every European country had adopted; and common law, a body of English decisions recorded century after century as local magistrates settled quarrels in country districts and villages throughout the land. Four times a year students were examined on Roman and common law. The questions were so simple that to answer them required only a little study.

One other requirement was made of students. They had to dine together at one of the halls in the Inns of Court at least six times each term. In former times this custom had a purpose. Then instructors would sit with students at dinner to discuss cases and legal points. But in the nineteenth century these occasions had become mere tradition. Students had no questions to ask and instructors sat together at their own tables.

The first time Mohandas dined with his fellow students he felt shy and nervous. He was sure that the three gay, noisy boys at his table would make fun of him for refusing meat and wine. When he turned down his glass, a youth named Simpson seated next him whipped around to stare.

"I say, Gandhi—that's your name, isn't it?—don't you really want your share of wine? You pay for it, you know." Assured by Mohandas that he never touched wine, Simpson let out a whoop of joy and shouted to his companions, "By Jove, fellows, we're in luck to have this chap sit with us. That gives us an extra half bottle."

"You may have my share of the roast, too," Mohandas told them, relieved to find that his peculiarities were making him popular.

Not all of them, however. The next time he dined at the hall he arrived with a pile of law books under his arm which he was taking to his room to study.

At sight of him Simpson whistled shrilly. "Dash it,

Gandhi, you're not really going through this stuff!" He snatched up one of the fat volumes. "Look, you chaps, he's actually reading Roman law in Latin!"

Laughing derisively, one of the other students at the table said, "Let me tell you, Gandhi, that I passed the last examination in Roman law by spending two weeks on a printed summary. Why do you grind like this?"

Mohandas turned off the question with a joke. He knew better than to admit to his lighthearted companions that he studied hard through sheer interest. Once or twice at the first dinner meeting he had tried to discuss a puzzling legal case and had been promptly snubbed. Nobody was interested in anything the dark-skinned foreigner had to say. He sat in silence while talk of parties, theaters, and races, expressed in incomprehensible slang, swirled around him. Mohandas felt no resentment. He had abandoned forever all idea of being like the Englishmen and was quietly enjoying London in his own way. Now that he had learned to live on less than a dollar a day his conscience was clear. He loved his studies. And his world was expanding.

One English group received him cordially. They were vegetarians on principle. Gandhi even persuaded them to form a club and elect as president Sir Edwin Arnold, one of the most distinguished British scholars of that day. Arnold was a specialist in Indian culture and had translated into English the most famous part of the great and ancient Indian epic.

At an evening gathering among Indian friends Mohandas spoke of knowing Sir Edwin Arnold. Two of the young men there were much excited. "You have met him!" cried one of them. "My brother and I are reading Sir Edwin's translation of the *Gita.* Why don't you come and read the original poem with us?"

"Alas!" replied Mohandas. "I haven't read the *Gita* either in the original or in the language of my province. But I should love to try to read with you anyway."

Thus began a new and vivid interest for young Gandhi. The poem, of which he had heard all his life, awakened fresh feeling for the Hindu religion. In turn that fervor made him curious about other faiths. He read the New Testament with profound sympathy and determined to study the Koran, sacred book of the Mohammedans. Alone in his tiny room, Gandhi thought deeply of the mighty leaders who had guided men, and he began to long for knowledge of the spiritual world. A kind of happiness he had never known before awoke in his heart.

His special friend, who had been out of London for two months, noticed a change in Mohandas the moment he saw him again. "What's been happening to you, Gandhi?" he asked. "You look so—well, so alive."

Mohandas stroked his little dark mustache. He could not speak of his new interest to this young man who had no feeling for religion. "Perhaps I'm beginning really to enjoy London," he replied. "Every day I walk miles through the noisy streets or along the river. This big, ugly city stands for the power of England, hard and determined. But I like the people, especially the workers and the ones in the slums. They love to joke. They are kind."

After a searching glance, his friend said, "Yes, you are more at home in the Western world now. Why don't you take a run over to Paris while you're here and get a first-hand impression of the French?"

Although months passed before he could act on this suggestion, it pleased Mohandas. With elaborate care he planned the cheapest possible trip. The instant he arrived at the French capital he bought a map and began a walking tour of boulevards, gardens, and famous avenues. He was shocked to find the famous Eiffel Tower so hideous and was happily surprised at the beauty of the cathedrals and chapels.   The simple reverence of people kneeling in prayer, whether they were well clad or in rags, moved him deeply.

After this excursion the approach of the final law examinations seemed very rapid. Mohandas was not in the least fearful of them. In the quarterly examinations his marks had always been high. But now that he was well versed in the theory of law he had begun to realize how little he knew about practicing it. The thought of having to do so was like a nightmare. Yet it was with the leaping joy known only to the exile that he made arrangements to take ship for home as soon as all the last formalities were over.

Early in May of 1891 he took his examination. In June he received his marks. They were very high. On June 10th he went through the ceremony of being "called to the bar" and next day he was formally enrolled in the high court. This meant that he had been judged worthy to practice law on a par with British attorneys. His own self-judgment was quite different, but he managed to bear himself with quiet dignity. On June 12th he boarded a ship for Bombay.

The homeward trip was different in every way from the

voyage to England three years before. The small-town boy who was afraid to face the dining saloon had turned into a well-dressed, experienced young man who spoke English fluently and followed British customs with ease. Even greater than this outward alteration was his inner change. At nineteen, he had started off with a gay sense of adventure. Now at twenty-two, the torture of self-doubt kept him tossing restlessly in his berth night after night.

"How can I support my wife and little son?" he would ask himself. "I don't know Indian law and not much Indian history. It will take me years to be fit to practice." Only the thought of being once more with his beloved mother and his wife calmed his forebodings.

As the vessel steamed into the Bay of Bombay, Mohandas stood at the deck rail, tense with emotion. In spite of his anxiety, he looked with eager joy at the silhouette of the city. Above the bulk of railway stations, hotels, and warehouses rose the mosques, burial temples, and marble towers characteristic of the many religious groups dwelling in every Indian city. Across the deck a hot offshore breeze swept the peculiar blend of incense and spices which was the smell of the bazaars. Ah, yes, this was India!

There was his brother on the wharf. Mohandas scurried down the gangplank to meet him. But even as they exchanged greetings, there was something in his brother's face that frightened him.

"You have bad news for me!" he cried.

"Yes, my brother. It was useless to wire you and disturb you during examinations. Our mother. . . . She died some weeks ago."

Grief over this loss ushered in a period which tried young Gandhi's soul to the utmost. Only the happiness of being with Kasturbai and his baby son kept him from despair. He had correctly foreseen the difficulty of starting the practice of law. Neither in his own home town nor in Bombay could he get anything better than routine work to do. He prepared briefs for other lawyers and drew up petitions for groups who wanted help from the local government. Little by little he began earning enough to cover expenses. But he saw no future in such work.

One hot evening his bitterness boiled into speech. He came home to find his brothers, their wives, and Kasturbai on the veranda. The women in their delicate chiffon saris, the men in loose shirts and the odd type of cotton trousers called dhotis, all looked cool and comfortable. With a violent gesture Mohandas hurled his English coat and vest into the arms of a startled servant and tore off his collar.

Facing his relatives, he burst out, "I hate this job of handing petitions to those high and mighty officials. What do they care whether the poor peasants are overcharged by landlords and cheated in the market? Less than nothing!"

Leaning forward, Kasturbai asked timidly, "Do you mean English officials, my husband?"

"No," he answered in a voice now more gloomy than violent. "I mean all of them. The Indians are just as bad—hirelings of spoiled princes and little officials who try to copy the toplofty British! They all make a petty, unloving, mean little world where it is very hard to get a mite of justice for those who have no power and no voice."

Kasturbai had moved away to pour him a cool drink from

a big pitcher on a stand. He took it from her and accepted the cushion she brought out. Something about her patient gentleness touched him. Even in the midst of the quick comments his brothers were making, he kept thinking of his wife. He had not given her a very happy time in these eighteen months since his return. For one thing, he had been determined to teach her to read and write. Although she was so quick at most of her feminine activities, she was very slow to learn her letters and this tired him out.

"You would much rather play with the children in this house than teach me!" she had said not long ago. He could not deny it. When he was teaching his son and his nephews games and physical exercises, he felt happy and at peace with the world. Then the old house rang with laughter and troubles were forgotten. Poor little Kasturbai, he must be more patient with her! She set him a good example, always gentle with him and so devoted to their new little baby!

It was not long after that explosive evening when his elder brother sent word to him one morning to come to his office. "I have a letter here," he said to Mohandas, "which contains the offer of a job. But I don't suppose you will even consider it."

The writer of the letter was a member of the firm of Dada Abdulla and Company. They were Mohammedan merchants who owned a big business in South Africa. The letter described a lawsuit the company had started against another firm of merchants. Abdulla claimed that he was owed four hundred thousand dollars by that firm. Since the suit had dragged on for some time, Abdulla's partner wrote to say that perhaps Mohandas Gandhi might go out to

South Africa and lend a hand. He spoke English and knew English law. Even if his legal advice did not prove necessary, he could handle the firm's English correspondence.

Mohandas studied the letter. Looking up doubtfully, he said, "This is no opening for a lawyer. I'm wanted to serve the company as a kind of clerk." Receiving a silent nod from his brother, he went on, "All the same, I'll talk the matter over with the man. He's the partner who lives here in India, I see."

Mohandas saw that his brother was pleasantly surprised at his willingness to seek the interview. When he returned from seeing Abdulla's partner, he surprised his entire family, for he had decided to accept the offer. In addition to all expenses he had been offered six hundred dollars for a year's work. This was more than enough to cover the support of Kasturbai and the children.

"I think it will be good experience," said Mohandas. "Anything that will lift me out of this rut sounds attractive. Besides," his eyes took on a faraway look, "something tells me this is a necessary step."

He clung to that faith through the pain of parting so soon again from Kasturbai. At Bombay he boarded a ship bound for South Africa and was assigned a first-class cabin. The captain seemed to take a liking to him from the beginning and played chess with him every day. With this friendliness and the charm of the southern seas, the youthful traveler found the voyage delightful. Yet it was long-drawn-out, and he was glad when at last the ship docked at Durban, the chief port of the province of Natal.

A large crowd was waiting on the wharf, and the instant

the gangplank was in place groups of Indians rushed on board to greet friends and relatives. Mohandas watched them eagerly. Would a representative of Abdulla and Company come to meet him? After a bit he noticed a portly middle-aged man in a high turban making his way through the crowd to speak to the captain. Everyone was bowing to him with great deference, but he paid no heed. With the captain, however, he laughed and talked a moment as if they were old friends.

Suddenly he turned and stared straight at Mohandas. Then he moved swiftly toward him. "I am Sheth Abdulla," he announced.

Grateful to be welcomed, Mohandas greeted him in the warm, smiling fashion which had always won him friends. But the heavy face into which he looked wore no smile. The big black eyes were measuring him from head to foot.

Then, without a word, the merchant waved his hand imperiously in the direction of the shore and turned toward the gangplank. In silence Mohandas followed him. Why was the Sheth not pleased to see him? Was this African venture to end before it had even begun?

CHAPTER III

In the office of his mercantile company Abdulla waved Mohandas to a seat at the table opposite him. Gravely he commanded, "Please show me now the papers concerning your employment which you say my partner sent me."

Promptly Mohandas took the closely written sheets from his small valise and handed them over. Then he sat back to watch the Sheth. Slowly and silently the man's lips formed each word. At the end of each sentence he would pause and reflect. Obviously the merchant was almost illiterate.

At last with a disapproving headshake the Mohammedan looked up. "I still cannot understand why you are here, Mohandas Gandhi. We have lawyers. They are good. Our case goes as usual. What work could I give you to do?"

In an abashed tone Mohandas repeated what the partner had said. "It was his idea," he murmured, "and he persuaded me to accept the post for a year."

For a long moment Abdulla's gaze traveled up and down

the small, slim figure before him. In his frock coat, black trousers, and stiff-collared shirt, Mohandas looked like a boy dressed in grown-up clothes. His only departure from an English costume was to wear a turban wound in Hindu fashion.

"Look how you are!" burst out the merchant. "You have very good clothes. You travel first-class. You will be a great expense to us."

Laughter leaped into the young man's eyes and voice. "Oh, have no anxiety on that score. I know how to travel and live on very little money. Tell me, Sheth Abdulla, where is the case to be tried?"

"In Pretoria, capital of the Transvaal. That is another thing." The Mohammedan spread out his hands. "If you go to Pretoria to work with the lawyers, I shall not be there to watch you. How can I tell what use you will be to us or how honest you are? Perhaps the merchants we are suing will get you over on their side!"

This bald expression of doubt had driven all smiles from Gandhi's face. Studying the merchant's shrewd expression, he reflected that the Sheth could not have built up the richest and largest mercantile house in South Africa without ability, honesty, and hard work. It was a pity that a man of high quality had so suspicious a nature.

"You will judge me correctly in time, Abdulla Sheth," said Mohandas gently. "I truly think I may be of service to you. Otherwise I should never have accepted your partner's offer."

Abdulla shrugged, sighed, rose to his feet, and announced that dinner and a bedroom were being provided.

Indeed, the unwelcome guest was treated very kindly. Within twenty-four hours Abdulla's manner had changed into something like respect. On the second evening the two discussed the Mohammedan religion, and the young Hindu's sympathetic interest was a happy surprise to Abdulla.

On the third day the merchant capitulated to Mohandas. "Since you are to work on our court case," said he as if he had never questioned the matter, "it would be well for you to see a British court in South Africa. Come with me this morning."

"With pleasure," replied Mohandas and dropped his eyes to hide their twinkle of joy and amusement.

Hardly had they been seated in the courtroom when Mohandas found the British magistrate staring at him in a curiously hostile way. The magistrate sat on a raised platform, listening to evidence presented on the current case. But he kept constantly turning back to glare at the visitor.

Suddenly Mohandas saw the magistrate lean forward to point a thick finger at him and heard him say sternly, "You must remove your turban."

In amazement Mohandas shot a glance around the room. Several Mohammedans and several clerks belonging to the Parsi religion also wore turbans. Why was he singled out for reproof? Indignantly he replied, "Sir, I see no reason to remove my turban and I refuse to do so."

"You will please remove it!" roared the magistrate.

At this Mohandas arose and left the courtroom.

Abdulla hurried after him into the corridor, caught his arm, and pulled him down beside him on a stone bench. "You don't understand," he gasped breathlessly. "Let me tell you what is back of the ruling they make on turbans."

Swiftly the merchant traced a sketch of the prejudice existing in the English colony of Natal. In the white man's eyes, Indians stood just a little higher than the native Negroes. At least they were allowed to vote for Assembly members and Negroes had no vote of any kind. But the English and Dutch descendants who ran South African affairs could make no further distinctions among darkskinned people. All Indians, whether ignorant mine workers, servants, or highly educated clerks at court, were merely inferiors and were addressed by the contemptuous names of "coolie" or "Sammi." Parsis and Mohammedans, however, enjoyed one privilege. Because their way of dressing was thought to have a religious significance, they alone were permitted to wear turbans anywhere, even in the courtroom.

As Mohandas listened, his dark eyes sparkled with anger. "The magistrate insulted me!" he cried. "Any such rule is an insult to a free man."

"True," said Abdulla soberly. "Here life is not fair for Indians."

"Probably," growled Mohandas, "I'd better throw away my turban and top my English dress with a hat!"

"No! No!" protested the Sheth. "You would then discourage those of us who insist on wearing turbans. Besides, an English hat would degrade you. You would look like a waiter."

A smile dawned in Gandhi's eyes. His employer must be a snob. Why should it be degrading to look like a waiter? On the other hand, the merchant had a manly hatred of knuckling under to the English. Feeling quite calm again, Mohandas said, "Very well, I'll keep on my turban and I'll write at once to the Durban newspaper to protest such insulting rules made by the court."

"Truly?" The Mohammedan flung an awed look at the young man. "You have courage. And of course you know their language. Perhaps your protest will have weight and will also put heart into others."

The letter was written and the fair-minded editor published it. But before learning its effect, Mohandas had started on the long trip to Pretoria where the Abdulla Company's suit was to be tried.

In those days few railroads had been built in South Africa and there were few passenger trains. Grasping the first-class ticket which Abdulla had insisted on buying for him, Mohandas bade good-by to his employer and climbed aboard the sleeping car. He had been told that in order to have his berth made up he must rent bedding from the agent at the next station. But, remembering that Abdulla had called him expensive, he resolved to save the money for bedding by sitting up all night.

When the train made its first stop, an Englishman got into the compartment, stared haughtily at Mohandas, and beckoned to the conductor in the corridor.

"Look here, now!" barked the Britisher. "I'm not going to travel in a compartment with a colored man. Put this coolie in a second-class car where he belongs!"

With a careless glance at the small figure in the corner, the conductor said, "Of course, sir. Hey, Sammi, come along to the next car."

"Certainly not!" Mohandas fixed indignant eyes upon the two men confronting him. "I was sold a first-class ticket and am entitled to ride here."

"That makes no difference," bellowed the conductor. "Come! Will you leave this car or must I call the station police?"

"That you will have to do, for I am certainly not going to give up my rights willingly," Gandhi said firmly.

Staring out of the window at the lights of the station, Mohandas waited rigidly for what was coming. Ten minutes later he was on the station platform, watching the tail lanterns of the train disappear. He had refused to enter the second-class car, and the train pulled on without him. The stationmaster took charge of Gandhi's luggage. Forlornly clutching his bag, the young man went into the empty waiting room. It was a cold night in this hilly region and an icy wind swept through the cracks of the building. Shivering and sleepless, he sat pondering the incident.

Wasn't it weak to swallow these insults? Why should he stay in such a country? For a time he thought longingly of home. Then he suddenly decided that to indulge the wish to escape was sheer cowardice. He simply could not allow so stupid a matter as color prejudice to change his chosen course.

Next morning as soon as the telegraph office was open, Mohandas was ready with two written messages. One was to the general manager of the railroad, protesting the injustice he had suffered. The other was directed to Abdulla. Both messages took effect. The railroad manager wired the stationmaster that he must assure Gandhi's safe arrival at his destination. Abdulla was even more helpful. He saw to it that several Indian merchants met Gandhi at the station with offers of entertainment and comfort.

"We have all been through just such bad times," they told him. "White men act as if we were dirt under their boots."

"But why is it so different here?" asked Mohandas in a bewildered tone. "In England I received no such treatment. I went everywhere without question or objection."

One of the older merchants said quickly, "Ah, but here white men are afraid of us. They are far in the minority and have to stamp on us to show who is superior."

On the advice of his new acquaintances, who took him to the evening train, Mohandas hired a roll of bedding. By good luck he found no one to object to his presence in the sleeping car. But next day after he left the train for a stagecoach which ran to Johannesburg, trouble began again.

In vain he showed his first-class ticket. "Oh, no!" snapped the conductor. "You can't sit inside with white people, ticket or no ticket. Sit outside there beside the coach box. That's my regular place, but I'll take your seat inside."

With a heavy heart Mohandas climbed into the seat behind the driver. Again conflict raged in his heart. He felt unmanly to accept in silence such an outrageous affront. On the other hand, he knew it was wise to get the journey over on any terms. Grimly he watched the grassy valleys between eroded hillsides and, as the coach lumbered its slow way up and up to higher levels of the land, he felt dampness and cold seep into his bones.

In the afternoon the stagecoach stopped at a small town
to change horses. The conductor, who had been laughing
with two black-bearded Boers, as the Dutch farmers were
called, lighted a long pipe. Just before the coach started on
again, he beckoned to Mohandas. "Hey you, Sammi! Sit
down here on the step. I need your seat now, for I've got
to smoke out here." As he spoke, he spread a dirty piece of
sacking on the step for his first-class passenger.

Without budging from his seat, Mohandas began to
tremble with rage and nervousness. "You seated me here
yourself!" he cried. "Even though I had a ticket for an inside seat. Now you want me to sit at your feet while you
smoke. I will not do it."

"You will, though!"

With a yell, the conductor struck first one of Gandhi's
ears and then the other with sharp blows. Seizing his arm,
the man tried to drag him from his seat. Clinging for dear
life to the coach box, Mohandas resisted. He felt as if his
wrist bones would snap. Shaking him, cursing him, the conductor pulled and jerked.

All at once voices rang out from within the coach. "Stop
that! Let him alone, conductor!" "He's in the right, man.
Don't beat him!" "Look, if you want him to move, let him
come take his own seat here with us."

The conductor let go his victim's arms. For a moment he
stood scowling and threatening vengeance. Then he pushed
the driver's Negro boy out of his seat on the other side of
the coach box and sat down there. The poor Hottentot
crouched on the step. Panting and terrified, Mohandas sat
rubbing his bruises. What would this creature do to him at
the end of the trip?

Two more hours went by. It began to get dark. At last, as the coach swung around a curve in the road, the lights of the town sparkled in the dusk. In a few moments the journey ended in front of a tavern. Afraid to move, Mohandas looked fearfully around to see where the conductor was. At that moment he caught sight of a number of men in white turbans and heard the sound of an Indian greeting. Eagerly he sprang down and was surrounded by a friendly group.

"Abdulla Sheth sent us word of your coming!" said one of the men. "We have come to take you to his friend's shop where you can stay."

Gratefully Mohandas strode along with them. The instant he had greeted his host at the shop, he asked for paper, pen, and ink. Thereupon he wrote the agent of the coach company, told him what had happened on the trip, and asked for a proper seat inside the coach for the next day's journey to Pretoria. A clerk took the note at once to the agent's office.

"You are certainly a fighter!" said his host, the merchant. "Never have we known an Indian to protest."

While they were at dinner, an answer came from the agent. Mohandas was told that in the larger coach running next day he would get proper accommodations. That promise was kept. By the next evening he was in the big, strange town of Johannesburg.

No one was at the coach station to meet him. Although he had the address of a Mohammedan merchant in the town, he felt it was too late to go there. He took a cab to the Grand National Hotel and entered the lobby lighted by bright gas lamps. At the desk marked "Manager" he asked for a room. As he did so, he saw out of the corner of his eye a tall blond Englishman make an eloquent grimace of scorn.

After a scrutinizing glance, the manager said with gentle politeness, "So sorry, but we are quite full up here tonight."

Mohandas understood. Again it was a matter of his dark skin. With a nod and shrug, he hurried out and found his cab waiting. He gave the driver the merchant's address and was soon bouncing over cobblestones and dust through half-lighted streets. In the depths of his sore heart he was asking, "If an English-speaking man in European dress is so disdained, what happens to some poor Indian who cannot speak the language?"

Bright shone the lamps in the shop where the cab stopped, and a cordial welcome was given the traveler. Mohandas related what had happened at the hotel and was startled by the merchant's roar of laughter.

"How on earth did you expect to be admitted to a first-class hotel?" he asked. Then, sobered by the look on Gandhi's face, he said patiently, "You'll have to face our situation. Those of us who are in South Africa to make money manage to put up with insults from white men. But a person like you, well, perhaps you won't be able to stand them."

The merchant advised Mohandas to travel to Pretoria in a third-class compartment in order to avoid trouble. But Mohandas would not listen and said he meant to continue his fight for personal justice. Within the next hour he had written a letter to the stationmaster stating that, since he always traveled first-class, he would like to receive in person a proper ticket from the stationmaster next day. Off went one of the shop employees to deliver the letter by hand.

"This journey of mine," explained Mohandas, "has been one series of protests against unjust treatment. I have hoped to break the ice of prejudice against Indians. If we let everything go in silence, we'll never be recognized as human beings."

Next morning he and the merchant went to the station. At the ticket window Mohandas asked for a first-class seat to Pretoria. The man in charge leaned across the counter with a little smile.

"You sent me a note last evening, didn't you?" he asked. At Gandhi's nod, he said quietly, "I am not from the Transvaal. I am a Hollander and appreciate your feelings, for you are a gentleman. I'll sell you a first-class ticket on one condition. If the conductor will not accept it and makes you travel in a third-class coach, you must not write a protest to the railroad or involve me in any way."

"I promise that gladly," said Mohandas and took the ticket.

"Well," murmured the merchant with a look of admiration, "you have won so far and I wish for you a safe, peaceful, and undisturbed trip."

With beating heart Mohandas took his seat in a first-class carriage. The only other passenger in the compartment was a well-dressed Englishman. He looked up from his newspaper, nodded to the newcomer, and went on reading. A moment later the conductor stood in the doorway, glowering at the intruder. Without a word, he jerked his thumb in the direction of the third-class car. Quickly Mohandas whipped out his first-class ticket.

"Your ticket doesn't matter, Sammi," growled the conductor. "Remove yourself to the third-class car at once."

Before Mohandas could speak, the Englishman flung down his paper and glared at the conductor. "What do you mean by troubling the gentleman?" he snapped. "His ticket gives him the right to be here and I do not mind his traveling with me in the least." Leaning forward, he said to Mohandas, "Make yourself comfortable just where you are."

Gandhi's dark eyes flashed the man a look of appreciation. This was the kind of Britisher he always had admired. In a quiet voice he thanked the man and took out a book to read.

From the doorway where he still stood, the conductor was staring unbelievingly at the Englishman. In a low voice he growled, "Well, if you want to travel with a coolie, it's nothing to me." With that he disappeared.

All the way to Pretoria the two passengers sat opposite one another reading in silence. Mohandas enjoyed every moment of it.

Early dusk had fallen as the train pulled into the Pretoria station. By the time Mohandas reached the platform with his bags, all the other passengers had left. For an instant he looked around in eager expectation. But no one from Abdulla and Company had come to meet him. Suddenly he realized that this was Sunday and it had not seemed right to disturb anyone. What should he do? Probably no hotel would admit him.

As he handed his ticket to the collector, he asked timidly if there were a place where he might spend the night.

"I'm sorry," murmured the official, "I don't believe I can direct you to one."

At this dark news Mohandas felt himself dropping into an abyss of isolation. Then just behind him a pleasant voice said in English, "I can direct you, sir. I think I can help you."

Mohandas whirled around to look up into the smiling face of a tall Negro whose smile gleamed in the dusky light. "I'm an American," went on the soft voice. "If you are alone here and a stranger, I'll guide you to a hotel owned by an American I know and I'm pretty sure he'll give you a room."

"That is very kind of you, indeed," replied Mohandas warmly.

Presently the two were entering the lobby of Johnston's Family Hotel. The Negro walked up to the proprietor and spoke to him in a low tone. The next moment the proprietor walked up to Mohandas.

"I have a room for you," said he, "but I'll have to explain that, although I myself have no color prejudice at all, my living depends on pleasing my European guests. I'm afraid I can't serve you in the dining room without offending them."

"That is understandable," said Mohandas. "I'm glad enough to be able to stay here tonight. If you'll serve dinner in my room, I'll be quite satisfied."

But Mohandas had not been long in his room when the smiling proprietor invited him to the dining room. "I inquired of my guests and none made any objection to your dining there," said he in a pleased tone.

As he sat enjoying the good meal, Mohandas mused upon the events of his first weeks in South Africa. Insults had certainly been offset by courtesy and kindness. Nevertheless, he had had a bird's-eye view of his countrymen's sufferings which had shocked him to the marrow. And for himself, what about the British lawyer who served Abdulla and Company? Would he prove prejudiced also, or might there be a chance to work with him?

Even during those few days in Durban, Mohandas had begun to study a few details of the suit. It interested him keenly. Since the case involved intricate accounts, he had bought a textbook and had given himself such an intensive course in the mysteries of debit and credit that he could understand the basis of Abdulla's claim. Somehow, he felt that with his knowledge of Indian nature he might make a definite contribution to the settlement of this quarrel. If only Mr. Baker, the lawyer, would accept him as an ally!

Next morning young Gandhi knocked on the door of an office in a big brick building. On the glass was printed "A. W. Baker, Attorney at Law." Again he wondered what sort of Englishman he was about to meet. As the door swung open, his breath came quick. It seemed to him he stood on the threshold of an experience which might test him to the utmost.

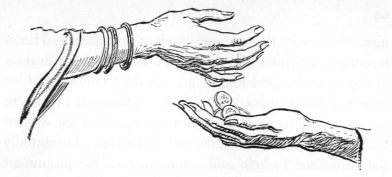

CHAPTER IV

"Ah, mr. gandhi, welcome to pretoria!"

With outstretched hand and a warm smile, the English attorney greeted the new member of Abdulla's legal staff. True, he said that just then he had no special work to assign. But his friendly interest launched Mohandas pleasantly into his new life.

Mr. Baker found a place for Mohandas in the house of a widow. She not only rented him a room but cooked vegetable meals for him. Moreover, the lawyer, who was an earnest church worker and missionary, took Mohandas to his religious group. He and a young Quaker named Coates made every effort to win over their new friend to the Christian religion.

To both men Mohandas said, "I am happy to meet with you and join in the prayers. But I was brought up a Hindu. I must study my own religion more deeply before I consider any connection with another faith."

Yet Gandhi was deeply grateful for the strong impulse these Englishmen gave him to go on with his meditations and religious studies. Struggle for a livelihood had absorbed him. Now every day he read modern and ancient Hindu teachings, the Bible, and the Koran. What such cultivation of the spirit inspired first of all was deep concern for his people in the Transvaal. He told the influential Indians to whom he brought letters of introduction that he wanted a complete picture of Indian life in Pretoria. Delightedly they promised to help and summoned all the prominent traders to meet at the house of a wealthy Mohammedan.

One by one Gandhi discussed with them different problems which faced his countrymen. First he talked of the need of improving sanitary conditions. "Let us learn how to do this from the Westerners!" said he. "They are not only personally clean but they dispose of all waste in a way which prevents bad odors, dirt, and disease. We must do away with the shocking conditions I have seen among Indians in this town. Those of us who have advantages of education, home training, and a good income should help our poor, ignorant fellow countrymen."

At last Mohandas came to the message deepest in his heart. This was Indian unity. "There is too much division amongst us!" he cried. "Why should we be kept apart by differences in birth, family tribes, and religion? Let us form a league representing every group. Then when we protest about unjust rulings to the authorities we may get a hearing."

Eagerly his audience listened. It was decided at once to hold regular meetings for all Indians living in Pretoria. Between these gatherings and his own personal visits Mohandas was able in a few months to know every single Indian in the town—servants, learned clerks, wealthy merchants, and scavengers. At first he was not sure just what he could do for them, but he felt that the way would be shown him. If only he could learn to be a better pupil in his lonely school of wisdom!

He tried one day to explain this to Mr. Baker. "If one really gets hold of a truth," he said, "one must apply it to daily life and to all dealings with other people. Then it is a living truth."

Mr. Baker seemed much impressed with this statement. The Englishman's personal friendship was now bearing fruit in work. Mohandas was given the task of translating into English all the correspondence exchanged by the two warring merchants. After prolonged study of the facts, Mohandas was completely convinced that his employers had a just claim.

He then set about finding how this could be proved to the judge who would decide the case. As he pored over the papers prepared by Mr. Baker and studied both law books and reports on similar court decisions, he felt he was getting that grasp of law he had been so aware of needing. Yet the more he learned about legal methods, the more anxious he was about Abdulla and his partners.

In a conference with Baker one morning he voiced his dismay. "If this case goes to court, might it not drag on for years? Lawyers on each side can find so many ways to continue their arguments indefinitely."

Baker looked into the eager face. "Yes," he agreed, "I suppose the trial might continue a long time."

"And think how costly that would be!" groaned Mohandas. "Both parties might be absolutely ruined."

Baker shrugged. "People must expect to pay if they bring a suit to trial."

Much as he liked this pious man, Mohandas was shocked at such indifference. Lawyers, he mused, are like leeches living on the blood of their clients. It seemed to him that the two merchants were foolish not to get together and settle their differences without paying the huge fees required by a court trial. He resolved to persuade them to do so.

Within the week he interviewed the chief representatives of both mercantile houses in Pretoria. To each of them he said, "Why don't you choose a good man whom you both trust, to arbitrate your quarrel? Save yourselves from the ruinous mistake of taking the suit to court."

This was an altogether new idea to both parties. They listened in astonishment. Although neither one would promise to consider the suggestion seriously, Mohandas felt, as he left first one and then the other, that each man was really interested.

By this time Gandhi's small figure in frock coat and Hindu turban had become familiar to everyone in Pretoria. Mr. Coates, the Quaker, often sought his company. They both enjoyed a brisk evening walk through the short, lighted streets of the provincial town to one of the near-by hills, bare except for the fields some Boer had managed to irrigate.

On one of these walks young Coates said, "One thing disturbs me about this pleasant exercise. It is, I regret to say, against the law for you, an Indian, to be on the streets after nine o'clock at night."

"Indeed!" exclaimed Mohandas. "Here as in Durban there is a curfew for the undesirables? Since I've not yet studied the regulations to keep us in our proper places, tell me what else we're forbidden to do."

Coates replied in the muffled voice of discomfort. "There are certain streets where you are not supposed to walk, particularly the one where the Boer president lives." Before Gandhi could ask where that street was, Coates burst out, "You know the Boers are responsible for such nonsense. Englishmen haven't even the vote in the Transvaal. Imagine how rotten that is!"

"Why?" asked his companion with a curious smile. "When you English took over Cape Colony, the Boers moved up to settle this section. It's theirs, isn't it?"

Sticking out his chin as he walked along in the moonlight, Coates suddenly looked very British. "But, my dear man, we have come into the Transvaal with capital and business experience to develop the gold mines and set up banks, law courts, all that makes civilization. Naturally we ought to have something to say about the government."

The two friends had reached the top of the slope now, and for an instant Mohandas gazed in silence down at the lights of the town and at the harsh, almost treeless landscape which no moonlight could transform into beauty.

Then he turned to his companion. "We Indians understand your wish for a share in the government. We have brought to the Transvaal, as to Cape Colony and Natal, a rich store of physical strength and energy for developing mines and vegetable gardens, for serving white men in various ways. Naturally we feel, as you do, that we'd like to have something to say about the regulations passed against us."

Although his tone was grave, a note of amusement could be heard in it. Catching that friendly irony, Coates gave a little laugh. "Yes, well, let's get back to the curfew regulation. I can't let you be arrested for walking with me at night. We must do something about it."

What they did was to go together to the state attorney, a Boer named Krause. The moment the two young men entered the office, Krause took one look at Mohandas and sprang up with a face alight with joy. "Mr. Gandhi! How good to see you again."

Mohandas recognized him instantly as one of his fellow law students in London. After a chat about old times the attorney was told the reason for the visit.

Krause looked pained. "Ah, Mr. Gandhi, such ordinances were made for peasants and porters and the like, not for a gentleman like you."

At once he dashed off a letter authorizing Gandhi to be out as late as he pleased at night without police interference. "Carry this letter with you, Mr. Gandhi, and show it if you are questioned. I'm sure you'll have no trouble."

That was a valued bit of special protection. But a few months after that note was written, Mohandas suffered the kind of brutal indignity with which his compatriots were threatened. Lately he had found a short cut from Mr. Baker's office to his boarding place through a residential street. He did not know its name and, although he noticed absently that a policeman was sometimes stationed at a

certain point, he gave the matter no thought. One evening, however, he was abruptly enlightened.

As he strode along at his usual fast pace, thinking hard
about the Abdulla case, a terrific blow on his shoulder
knocked him into the dust of the unpaved street. Bruised
and dazed, he sat up to find a Boer policeman towering
over him.

With a thick accent the man roared, "That teach you
maybe to obey law. No Indian walk past President Kruger's
house."

So that was his crime! Mohandas struggled to his feet.
At that instant he heard a familiar voice calling him from
near by. "I say, Gandhi, are you hurt?" Looking around,
he saw his friend Coates dismounting from his horse.

Coates bent over him anxiously. "What an outrage!"
He turned to glare at the policeman. "If this man, a distinguished lawyer, brings a complaint against you, I'll be
his witness. I saw the whole beastly thing. Oh, Gandhi, I'm
so sorry about this attack."

Mohandas was busily brushing the dust from his coat.
He saw at a quick glance that the policeman was pale with
consternation. "You need not be sorry, my friend," he said
gently. "It's time I shared these experiences with my countrymen. It's not this poor man's fault. He has to enforce
the stupid regulations. I shall not make a complaint."

Coates gave him a look of deep admiration. "That's just
like you," he said. Then, turning to the policeman, he said
severely, "You should tell an Indian politely what the regulation is—not knock him down. Why behave like a brute?"

The policeman's shamefaced look and stammered apology drew a smile from Mohandas. "Never mind," said he. "I have already forgiven you."

Moving on down the street beside his friend, who was leading his horse, Mohandas could not hear one word Coates was saying. He was absorbed in the radiant peace flooding through his own being. That incident, the bewilderment on the blunt features of the policeman as he heard the words of forgiveness, had opened in Gandhi a vein of compassion such as he had never experienced before. He realized both the humiliations of his fellow Indians and the pitiful fate of those who had to enforce cruel and unjust regulations.

It was with renewed vigor that a few days later he again urged the representative of the Abdulla Company to arbitrate the dispute. He also renewed the same plea with the head of the rival company. Finally that man agreed to the idea and soon afterwards Abdulla's manager came to the same decision. The arbiter was chosen and in a short time handed down his judgment. It was in favor of Abdulla.

On the day of this triumph the victors held a celebration in the shop. Trays of sweetmeats, cakes, and spiced drinks were passed. Gandhi was praised and congratulated by everyone.

But presently the manager hushed the laughter and chatter by an outcry. "Look at our savior and guide here! He is not happy. His face is sad and he does not celebrate. Why? What is it?"

Mohandas looked around the circle of anxious faces. "I am thinking of the merchant who has lost the case," said he gravely. "If he has to pay out this huge sum all at once, he will be ruined. You have been friends and have done business together. Will his ruin profit you?"

Excited voices protested. "But ours is a just claim. The arbiter found it so. Would you have us give it up?"

"By no means." The youth of twenty-four looked pleadingly at the successful businessmen. "But could you not be merciful? Could you not let this debt be paid little by little so that your rival will be neither humiliated nor bankrupted?"

In the end his plea was heard. The Abdulla Company partners drew up easy terms of payment and felt happily noble. Members of the losing firm were grateful. And both sides acknowledged that Gandhi had led them wisely in every way. The final settlement was made for half the costs of a court trial.

After every detail had been worked out, Mohandas cabled his family that he was returning to India. He engaged passage, bade farewell to his friends in Pretoria, and by train and omnibus reached Durban on the coast of Natal. Abdulla Sheth gave him an enthusiastic welcome and told him he had arranged a farewell dinner for him.

Almost all the guests were Mohammedans, and Gandhi was the youngest man there. During a lull in the festivities he strolled into the Sheth's office and began looking over recent copies of local English newspapers on the table. Suddenly his eye was caught by a headline, "Indian Franchise." The item reported a bill before the assembly which took from the Indians in Natal their power to vote for assemblymen. Its passage would reduce Indians in this colony to the same powerless level as their compatriots in the Transvaal.

In dismay Mohandas rushed back to his host. "Abdulla Sheth," he asked excitedly, "is anything being done to work against the bill taking away our votes?"

Abdulla had no idea what he meant. Neither did the other guests. Everyone pressed around Mohandas to listen to his explanation.

As he finished, Abdulla with resigned shrugs and outspread hands said bitterly, "What can we understand of these things? We are unlettered men. All we can read in those newspapers are the daily market rates. Our eyes and ears are the English lawyers we hire. They would give us no warning of evil threatening us. We can do nothing."

"Ah, surely you aren't so helpless!" protested Mohandas hotly. "There are many educated young Indians in Natal who could work with you to oppose such a wicked bill!"

Abdulla shook his head and said sneeringly, "They pay us no attention. They are under the thumb of white men, all English, all in sympathy with the British government."

Depression swept over Gandhi. "All the same," he said, "these men are still Indians." As he spoke, he resolved not to spoil Abdulla's party by any more serious talk. After all, he was sailing home and it was none of his business. Nevertheless, he could not help sighing out, "If this bill passes, our lot in Africa will be harder than ever. It is one more nail in the Indian coffin."

"True!" "You are right!" "It is unbearable." The group pressed closer to him.

"Well, what do you advise?" asked Abdulla nervously.

As Mohandas hesitated, one of the Mohammedans cried out, "I know what should be done. Mohandas Gandhi should cancel his passage. Remain here. Stay and lead us and we will rise up behind you!"

With one voice the others said, "Yes, indeed yes! Abdulla Sheth must detain Gandhi."

A look of anxiety shadowed the shrewd face of the merchant. "Oh, no! It is not for me to detain him here. It is for all to do so. If he stays, his living must be seen to. He is a lawyer. Who will pay his fees?"

Not until later did Mohandas spare a chuckle over this speech. How afraid Abdulla was that he might be expected to support him! At the moment, however, he was only shocked at the word *fee*.

"Do not speak of fees, Abdulla Sheth!" he answered quickly. "Work for the good of our people has no price. I could, if you wish, stay a month longer and organize a protest against this bill. Not a cent would I accept for such a service. But money must be contributed for a campaign. We may have to print leaflets of information, send telegrams, take tours by train and hired wagons, arrange meetings, and so on. I'll have to have many volunteers to help me."

"We will all help! Money will be given!" A chorus of glad voices filled the room. "Allah is great and merciful! Allah be praised! Mohandas Gandhi will stay and lead us."

Moved to the depth of his being, Mohandas thanked his friends. Then he said, "Let us start this moment. Give me a list of the young men in Durban and other towns. I also need names of all Indians who voted at the last election. There is no time to be lost."

Late that night in his small room in Abdulla's house, Mohandas lay on his narrow bed thinking over the strange turn in his fortunes. Had it happened by accident? He could not think so. Fate had ordained the evening's episode. He had promised to stay a month. But after the dinner party had turned into a lively committee meeting he was not so sure that he could do the job in a month. In fact, perhaps . . . yes, it was possible . . . a new career was opening for him in South Africa.

CHAPTER V

THE VERY NEXT EVENING THE FIRST SESSION OF VOLUNteer workers was held at Abdulla Sheth's house. The chairman of the meeting was a forceful Mohammedan regarded by all as the leader of the Indian community. With legs crossed under him, he sat on a huge low couch made of wood and covered with a rug. The others sat cross-legged on the floor.

Without delay Mohandas outlined his plan to prepare a petition and get it signed by as many Indians as possible. The volunteers were to take copies to them, explain the matter fully, and collect signatures.

After the meeting was over, one of the young men approached Gandhi. "I should like to ask you," said he, "how it is that for the first time in Durban, Indians of every group and religion are gathered here tonight. Hindus, Moslems, Parsis, Christians. I didn't know it was possible."

Triumph surged through Mohandas. "This is exactly

what we must work for—unity. Prejudice amongst us is really old-fashioned." He chuckled. "How can we expect the English to shake off prejudice unless we do so ourselves?"

Lively days of work followed. Volunteer workers rushed around in their own or hired carriages to get signatures, and copies of the petition were sent to both legislature and press. Although the newspapers published sympathetic comments, the bill depriving Indians of their vote passed the assembly with a large majority.

"Don't be discouraged, my friends," Gandhi said to everyone. "We have started activity. We are learning to work together. We'll now send a monster petition to the British secretary of state for the colonies in London, asking him to veto the bill."

By the time this petition was printed and sent to newspapers in both South Africa and India, Gandhi's month of volunteer work was over. But all the leaders in the battle said to him, "You cannot leave us now. You must stay and work with us."

Frankly Gandhi replied to them that he could not remain without financial guarantees for himself and his family. Since he would accept no pay for his services to his countrymen, the merchants solved the problem in another way. They turned over to him all of their legal business. Immediately Gandhi established himself in an office with a secretary.

Far more important was his next step. In order to argue cases in court with the same authority as that of English lawyers, he must be admitted as an attorney to the Supreme

Court of Natal. Since no dark-skinned man had ever before had the courage to make such an application, Mohandas was prepared for the sensation he created.

Indians in Durban gasped with excited admiration. But the conservative British were aghast. The Law Society, a powerful club of English attorneys, at once warned Gandhi it would oppose his application with all its influence. When the hearing was held before the Chief Justice of the Supreme Court, the Law Society made good its threat. Its most distinguished member opened the session. Eloquently he argued that it would disgrace the profession to allow a colored man to practice on the same level as a white attorney.

In the handsomely decorated courtroom Gandhi sat listening to this plea. Every muscle in his body was tense. A refusal of his application meant such loss of prestige that he could hardly imagine remaining in Natal. He studied the impassive face of the Chief Justice, framed in the white, curled wig which English custom demanded. How mighty he looked in his handsome robes! He was gravely studying Gandhi's credentials that lay on his desk: a notation of his enrollment in the high court of London, his certificate to serve as attorney in the courts of Bombay, the testimonials of character from English and Indian friends in South Africa.

As the voice of the lawyer ceased, the Chief Justice looked around the courtroom. Quietly he said, "The law makes no distinction between white and colored people. The court has therefore no authority to prevent Mr. Gandhi from being enrolled as advocate. We admit his application. Mr. Gandhi, you can now take your oath."

There it was once more—the noble spirit of Anglo-Saxon justice which Mohandas admired so much. It towered over the ugly prejudice which marred English behavior in this foreign land. Thrilled by the faith that it would always appear, no matter how dark the pattern of official acts, and tingling with the triumph of having blazed a path for other dark-skinned men who might one day practice law in South Africa, he went down to the judge's desk. Looking very small and young beside the Englishman with his robes and wig, he took the oath.

As soon as he had done so, the judge told him that as a practicing barrister, he must conform to the rules of the court regarding dress. Gandhi's Hindu turban must go.

With the friendly smile which always made people forget how plain he was, Mohandas unwound the folds of his headgear.

Outside the courtroom he found Abdulla in a state of divided emotion. He was bursting with pride that Mohandas had succeeded. Yet he was angry over the loss of the turban. "You should not have yielded!" he cried.

"I do not agree," replied Mohandas firmly. "The officer of the court has the right to demand that its customs be followed. I will save my energy for a fight over something important."

Gandhi's triumph inspired such enthusiasm among well-to-do Indians that they began to overwhelm him with requests for legal services. He was soon one of the busiest lawyers in Durban and was earning more than any English attorney. But to him the profession of law was merely the means to an end. His heart was in the work of improving conditions for his countrymen.

The cornerstone of this work was the organization which he founded almost immediately. This body, called the Natal Indian Congress, attracted to its monthly meetings Indians of all creeds from every corner of Natal. The regular dues of about fifteen dollars a year were increased by contributions from wealthy members and soon there was available a handsome sum for propaganda.

"We must put before the English people what we Indians have to endure in this country," Gandhi kept urging the congress. "After all, many of them are decent folk, but don't realize what is going on."

In response to his plea, a pamphlet describing all the injustices meted out to the Indians in South Africa was soon widely circulated among the British. Hand in hand with this sped another asking every fair-minded Anglo-Saxon to help the Indians retain their vote in Natal.

One day there burst into Gandhi's office a nightmarish figure—a dirty, half-naked Indian bleeding from several wounds. Through broken front teeth he poured out his pitiable story. He was the indentured servant of an Englishman who had brutally beaten him. Someone had told him that in Durban lived a wonderful man called Mohandas Gandhi and he had run to him like a hunted hare.

As Gandhi listened, he felt as if it were he himself whose flesh had been torn by blows. He had known of the hard lot of the indentured Indian worker. He realized that streams of them were sent from the two eastern provinces of India, Bengal and Madras, on a five-year contract to labor in South Africa at starvation wages. The contract forbade them to leave their employers under pain of imprisonment. But now for the first time Mohandas had direct, personal contact with one of these poor slaves. Tears were in his eyes as he assured the man he would protect him.

He did so with the utmost speed. After taking the man to a doctor who certified the nature of his wounds, Gandhi hurried to a magistrate. Thoroughly indignant, the English official said he would call the brutal employer before him. Gandhi, however, never wanted punishment for the offender. Justice for the victim was his goal. Presently he himself confronted the well-dressed employer in his Victorian parlor. Would he release the servant he had so abused? Plainly frightened, the man agreed without argument, and at once Gandhi succeeded in placing his protégé in the home of a humane Englishman of his acquaintance.

Reports of this case spread far and wide. At last indentured laborers felt that they could count on help in time of trouble. A stream of them poured into Gandhi's office and the pitiful stories they told gave him rich material for his battle with the government.

That battle was now joined in earnest. For in the year 1894 the Natal government made a new attack on Indian security. This time the victims were indentured workers. A law was proposed to place a severe tax on the man who had finished his five-year contract and wished to remain in South Africa as a free worker. As an indentured man he could earn a sum equal in American money to $28.80 a year. Yet the tax was set at $15.00 a year for every member of his family. It was plain that since the tax could not be paid, free workers would be driven out of the country the moment the contract was ended.

The shock of the proposed bill to the Indian population was immeasurable. And to their bewildered outcries many a fair-minded Englishman added his indignant protest. Gandhi, together with other farsighted Indians, saw exactly what was back of this tax. British industrialists wanted only enslaved laborers at starvation wages. All free Indians were considered rivals to white workers in trade, on farms, and in manual occupations. They were not wanted in Natal.

Everybody turned to Gandhi for leadership. "We'll never stop fighting this tax," he said firmly, "not if it takes years to win the battle."

Meanwhile, he had been heartened by the vigorous protest against the bill which resounded from India itself. Heretofore, leaders in his own country had seemed to him singularly indifferent to the sorrows of the South African group. Perhaps, he thought, if he went back for a visit he could win definite support for a campaign.

He had, however, a more personal reason for going. It was now three years since he had left Kasturbai and their two boys. Although his days were so crowded with work, although he would permit himself no sentimental repinings, he had never felt quite whole without his family. It was therefore with a joyful heart that he engaged passage back to India. He had arranged his work so well that he could look forward to a six-month leave. And when he came back it would be with his family.

With a full heart he looked once more upon his boyhood home, to which he rushed the moment he landed. There, wrapped in an embroidered sari fine as gossamer, Kasturbai welcomed him. He studied her fondly. How little she had changed since he had brought her here, a child bride. But the two boys!

"I left you a baby!" he said, swinging the younger child into the air. "And now you've had the cheek to become a man of five! As for you"—he turned his smile upon the elder boy—"you'll soon be as tall as I, you nine-year-old bean pole, and you might grow even handsomer than your father."

Merry as was the family reunion, still Mohandas could spare little time from his great crusade. He launched it by writing a small book known as the "Green Pamphlet," setting forth the plain facts about the Indian struggle in South Africa. Ten thousand copies were printed and they vanished in a flash. Some went to London where newspapers printed summaries. Then Gandhi began to shuttle across India from Bombay to Madras. He made it a point to meet the editors of all the influential newspapers that printed sympathetic interviews. Above all, he made personal contacts with the Indians who were leaders in education and politics.

The most famous of these was undoubtedly J. K. Gokhale. He was exactly Gandhi's age, twenty-seven, and like Gandhi was filled with nervous energy and an unbounded faith in the future of India. From the moment the two young men met they knew they were going to be friends for life. On nearly every point they saw eye to eye. For example, Gokhale cried passionately, "My friend, we can trust to the fairness of England. Only by working through her and with her can India win freedom." What was this but an echo of Gandhi's own faith?

At Poona, near Bombay, Gokhale organized a meeting where Gandhi addressed some of the most influential men of the day. It was only one of the many speeches he made during his six-month sojourn. Thanks to these speeches, his famous "Green Pamphlet," and feature stories about his work in newspapers, the young man who had left India only three years ago a penniless little lawyer was rapidly becoming a national figure.

His work of arousing interest in the South African struggle was going well. Suddenly it was interrupted by a disaster. A plague broke out in Bombay, and Gandhi volunteered to join the group trying to educate the people in his own town in sanitary methods of prevention. From visits to the homes of wealthy merchants and professional men he always returned to Kasturbai in a mood of violent indignation.

"Such filth," he would fume. "Here are wealthy men living in richly furnished houses that reek like pigsties. They know nothing of modern sanitation and if you try to tell them, they look insulted. For my part, I'm looking forward to visiting the Untouchables. I'm sure they'll be cleaner and they'll want to learn."

"The Untouchables!" cried Kasturbai, horrified. "Oh, surely, my husband, you wouldn't . . . even you wouldn't enter the house of an Untouchable!"

Kasturbai's shuddering horror arose from a deeply rooted Hindu social custom. For thousands of years followers of this ancient religion had been divided into four groups called castes. The Brahmin caste was the highest and, no matter what his occupation might be, a Brahmin could always say to himself, "I am the aristocratic descendant of the priests of Brahma."

The warrior or noble caste came next, and the third included professional men, traders, and farmers. It was to the third caste that Gandhi himself belonged. Laborers made up the fourth class.

No matter what he achieved, nobody born into a lower caste could ever progress to a higher one. A man always married within his caste. Most of his friendships were made within it.

Outside all the castes were the Untouchables and all the top groups united in loathing them. From time immemorial these poor creatures had been assigned to the filthiest jobs of the community. Whatever an Untouchable handled was at once polluted. If an Untouchable let down his water jar into a well, that well was forever poisoned for everyone else. These outcasts accepted their fate without protest as something ordained by the gods.

Now, as an assistant to the health officers, Mohandas entered an Untouchable's home for the first time in his life. He came back glowing to Kasturbai. "They're clean!" he cried. "I wish you could see the spotless floors and the pots and pans in these Untouchable huts! What's more, they are as eager to learn as children—very different from the rich Brahmins we visited!"

Kasturbai shook her head. "My husband, what will you do next? Perhaps invite an Untouchable to dinner!"

He flashed her a smile with mischief in it. "Prepare yourself, my girl. I've long thought no loving God ever approved of these hard and fast divisions between human beings. From now on I intend to fight this wicked caste system. We Indians have many things to overcome before Englishmen can respect us. Worst of all is our cruelty to these most neglected of God's children."

It was June when Gandhi had returned to India. In December he was again looking up at the high hills around the harbor of Durban and down at the curving beaches flanked by boulevards. Beside him at the railing on the ship's forward deck were Kasturbai and the two boys and a nephew. All four faces wore the same expression of awe at the sight of a foreign place, mixed with eagerness.

"Father," asked the older boy impatiently, "aren't we ever going to get off this ship? I thought when the doctor said nobody on board had the plague, we were going to land."

For a silent moment Mohandas looked down at his son. He had insisted that the boys adopt a costume something like that of the Parsis. In their leather shoes, trousers, and fitted coats, they looked, he thought, very civilized.

"You see," he answered slowly, "we sailed from Bombay where the plague was raging not long ago. The doctor doesn't wish to run any risk of our bringing disease into Durban."

With that Mohandas turned away. He had no wish to share with his family his certainty that it was not fear of the plague which was delaying permission to land. The captain had dropped a confidential hint that the mass of white residents in Durban were loudly protesting the arrival of more Indians. The captain's ship and another one anchored near it were both owned by the Dada Abdulla

Company and between them they had brought eight hundred Indians from Bombay. Day after day they had waited in the harbor. Everyone was bored and bewildered. Even the children knew that the time of quarantine had long passed.

As he walked down the deck, Gandhi saw the captain beckon to him. The man was frowning and shaking his head. "Feeling is ugly in Durban," he said in a low tone. "I've sent word that most of our passengers are old residents of the Transvaal and will go straight there. But the agitators won't believe it. They keep telling the mob that we're landing workers who will take jobs from white men." The captain looked toward shore and turned back to say, "I might as well warn you, Mr. Gandhi, that it's you they blame. There's been stuff in the newspapers about your stirring up hate for the British over in the homeland."

Looking into the captain's friendly eyes so full of anxiety, Mohandas caught a picture of his own danger. When the passengers finally stepped ashore, he would be the target of attack. A frenzied mob might stop at nothing. They might even kill him.

When harbor authorities finally signaled that the ships might land their passengers, Gandhi's first thought was for his family. They must not land in his company. It was with infinite relief that he accepted the captain's offer to see them safely into a carriage. They had all been asked to stay at the house of a friend.

"I'll see you there shortly," he said, as they started down the gangway.

Should he himself take the captain's advice and sneak off

the ship after dark? The idea was utterly repulsive to him. Yet he was still turning it over when the agent of the steamship line approached.

"The crowd has gone. There's no danger now, Mr. Gandhi. I'll go ashore with you and take you to your friend's house."

Encouraged by these assurances, Gandhi followed the agent down to the dock. The scene looked peaceful enough. The group of youths at the end of the dock was obviously bent on nothing more mischievous than the usual fun of watching a landing.

Then suddenly a rough voice rang out loud and clear. "Look, there he is! There's Gandhi!" Instantly one of the youths made a dash for the two men who were starting across the wharf. He was followed by all his companions, hunters who had unexpectedly fallen upon their quarry.

In spite of this assault, the agent managed to get Gandhi out to the street to a rickshaw. But the hunters surrounded the vehicle and frightened the rickshaw man away. Then they drove off the steamship agent. Now all alone, Gandhi faced those twelve or fourteen hoodlums.

He tried to walk away from them, but they pelted him at every step with stones, sticks, and rotten eggs.

Soon missiles were not enough. One of the boys grabbed off the Indian turban. Older fellows began to kick and pummel the frail figure. At last Gandhi sank unconscious to the ground. When he opened his eyes, he clutched at a fence railing and was trying hard to raise himself when he heard an Englishwoman's voice. "Stop, you cowards! Stop!"

In amazement he recognized the wife of the superintendent of police, always a warm friend of his. As if in a dream he saw his rescuer forcing her way between the hoodlums. Now she was by his side. Instantly she raised her umbrella and held it between him and the crowd. Thus shielded, she dared them to advance a single step.

At this very moment came the clatter of hoofs. Six mounted policemen, who had been called by an Indian spectator, galloped into view. This bodyguard carried Gandhi swiftly to the police station and from there to the Indian home where Kasturbai and the three boys were already settled.

Many friends had gathered in the house. One of them was the ship's doctor, who promptly treated Gandhi's injuries. The superintendent of police who had brought Gandhi there said he feared the mob would gather around the house. The prophecy was soon realized. Suddenly a hundred voices began to bawl, "Give us Gandhi or we'll burn down the house."

"You'll have to disguise yourself and escape by the back door, Mr. Gandhi," said the police chief. "Quick. I'll hold off the crowd till you get away."

A few minutes later a small figure in a constable's uniform slipped from the rear of the house. Gandhi never stopped until he reached the police station. He did not budge from it for two days. Then suddenly came astonishing news. London authorities had cabled that the Natal government must prosecute every man guilty of attacking Mr. Gandhi. Next day a lawyer called to say that if Mr. Gandhi would identify his persecutors, they would be arrested at once.

"Never," said Mohandas. "The members of that mob had been told lies about me. I wouldn't think of bringing charges against them."

By the time news of this statement got abroad, the *Natal Advertiser* had printed a favorable interview with Mohandas. In a twinkling the sentiment of Durban changed. Newspapers praised his forgiving spirit and condemned the violence of the mob. Wherever he went, distinguished Englishmen stopped him to apologize for the attack.

A crowded year followed Gandhi's stormy arrival in Natal. During that time he won none of the causes for which he had fought. Even so, the love felt for him by every type of Indian was more firmly established than ever. When, in 1897, war broke out between England and the Boers in the Transvaal, this devotion was sharply tested.

For Gandhi, foe of English oppression, Gandhi, who knew perfectly well that the English desire to control the diamond and gold mines of all South Africa was back of the struggle, took a course which shocked and bewildered both friends and followers.

CHAPTER VI

GANDHI INTENDED TO FORM AN AMBULANCE CORPS FOR service in the British army. This was the announcement which so stunned his followers. He made it in a speech to the Natal Indian Congress soon after the outbreak of war. Two sentences explained his attitude.

"Our one hope of freedom as a people," he said, "is through development within the British Empire. Therefore we must help defend it."

Some listeners were convinced by his argument. Others were willing to follow him blindly. Soon eight hundred indentured workers and three hundred free Indians were serving under the British flag in camps and hospitals. Indeed, together with their leader, many of them worked under fire. And so high was their standard of courage and devotion that they were universally praised by British military leaders and British journals.

No one cherished such praise more hopefully than did Gandhi. Surely after such proofs of Indian loyalty the British government could not remain deaf to Indian claims. Sometimes a skeptic would say to him, "Can you really expect generosity from vultures who are trying to snatch away treasures which belong to the Boers?" Then he would reply gently, "Yes, for I believe in the justice of the British people." Hearing himself say this, he would think of Gopal Gokhale, the great leader whose friendship he had made. He also believed in the ultimate fair dealing of England.

As it happened, the Indian ambulance corps was fated to have a short life. For soon the British abandoned violent military action in favor of a siege of the Transvaal, a blockade which would break the spirit of the brave and stubborn Boers. In the end they must surrender their free republic, their farms, and their gold and diamond mines.

During the years which followed the start of the Boer War, the pattern of Gandhi's life became ever simpler. The house in which he had installed his family was at first run in a somewhat luxurious way. Soon, however, his desire to be independent of comforts made him discontented with their fashion of living.

One morning while they were at breakfast Mohandas looked over to Kasturbai to say, "I think we'll have to get rid of our laundryman. He's outrageously expensive."

She lifted her eyebrows. "But why should we care about that? You are making a great deal of money these days, my husband."

"True enough, but does that give us the right to waste? I should rather give the money we spend on laundry to help humanity."

Shortly after this conversation Gandhi himself replaced the laundryman. The result of his first adventure with starch and an iron was a burst of laughter as he entered the courthouse. It came from every English attorney and Indian clerk who saw him come in.

"Where did you run into the blizzard, Mr. Gandhi?" called out one lawyer. "I believe," laughed another man, "you'd taste better without so much flour."

With woeful merriment Gandhi looked down at his coat. It was thickly flaked with starch. "Yes, I know I starched this shirt and collar too much and my iron wasn't quite hot enough. But wait and see. Before I'm through I'm going to be the peer of any laundryman in Durban."

Hand in hand with economies went his insistence that every member of his household take an active part in its daily chores. He taught his boys to make beds, clean their rooms, and help him with the laundry. And, though they may have secretly grumbled at first, they gradually came to see that physical work was good for everyone.

Upon Gandhi's little wife this stern program of daily life often laid a heavy hand. Brought up as a strict Hindu, she found it fearfully hard to accept the people her husband brought to stay at their home. English foreigners with their entirely different customs were bad enough. But when Mohandas brought home as a boarder a low-born Indian Christian, she very nearly revolted.

"We must take entire charge of his needs at first," explained Mohandas calmly. "The other Hindus in our house are not yet used to sharing life with such a person. We must prepare his meals, make his bed, empty the slops, and so on."

Kasturbai gritted her teeth. It never occurred to her to disobey her husband's command. Obedience was part of her training. But how could she manage to look pleased that first morning when she came downstairs from the new boarder's room?

Mohandas, meeting her at the bottom of the steps, cried out at the disgust on her face. "I shall not stand this nonsense in my house! God did not set up these distinctions between human beings. Man's prejudice did that. You must do these services gladly."

At her patience's end, Kasturbai shouted back, "Keep your house to yourself and let me go."

Then followed a terrible quarrel which reduced Kasturbai to tears and Mohandas to a repentance which he remembered all his life. Long afterwards he wrote sorrowfully of the blind selfishness which made him treat his wife sometimes as one born to grant his every wish. Yet slowly, as he grew to love her more wisely, he learned to make her his partner and comrade.

His fellow Indians were often puzzled by Gandhi's experiments in simple living. But they knew he had not undertaken them idly and felt no scorn for the impulses of a man they thought extraordinary. In a tone of special reverence both Mohammedans and Hindus spoke of the volunteer work he was doing at a hospital for indentured Indian workers. Every morning he spent two hours at this hospital. Here he made beds, bathed patients, and emptied slops. And by dint of hard study he even learned to mix simple prescriptions in the drug department.

It was in 1901, six years after he had brought his family to Durban, that Mohandas decided his field of greatest usefulness lay in India. Every Indian in Natal mourned the decision. By this time his associates were calling him Bhai, meaning brother, an intimate name which delighted Mohandas. Now, to show how much they loved him, they gave a farewell party and loaded him down with costly gifts. Kasturbai, too, received a splendid necklace.

Watches and bracelets, ornaments not only of gold and silver but of diamonds! As Gandhi looked down at these treasures spread out on the chest in his bedroom, he felt like some Aladdin who had accidentally rubbed the lamp and brought forth unwanted riches. What should he do with these baubles? How could expensive jewelry fit into a life which he was trying to make more and more simple? Restlessly pacing the floor, he finally received an inspiration. He would create a trust fund of his gifts for the benefit of the community.

But he knew his decision would be a blow for his poor little Kasturbai. Foreseeing trouble, he first enlisted the support of his two eldest sons. The two younger boys, born in Durban, were still too little to count in such matters. Both the older boys thought the community fund was a fine idea. Even with their aid, however, it was hard to meet his wife's storm of protest.

"You may not need these things," she cried, and angry tears stood in her eyes. "Your children may not need them. I can understand your not allowing me to wear them. But what about my daughters-in-law? They will be sure to need them. I was so happy to think we had gifts for them."

Gently Mohandas replied, "Surely we shall not have for our sons brides who insist on ornaments!"

Tenderly then he explained that her fate was joined to

that of a man who had chosen a stony path. He had forsaken forever all personal wealth and meant to live like the humblest of their countrymen. Slowly, tearfully, Kasturbai admitted that to give the jewels to the community was a noble ideal which she could not oppose. When she saw with what astonished gratitude the Indian community heard Gandhi's plan, she was reconciled. As they leaned over the ship's rail to wave good-by to friends on shore, her husband saw with relief that her face was wreathed with happy smiles.

Hardly had the Gandhi family reached their old home when Mohandas left to attend the most important political gathering in India. This was the annual meeting of the All-India Congress, held at that time in Calcutta.

The congress, organized in 1885, with the aid of British administrators, was the only body which gave Indians a chance to air political views. Even though it had no power whatsoever to affect decisions of the government, the organization had already won a certain amount of influence. The members were mostly well-educated, conservative men with comfortable incomes, who had profited by English rule. They did not support the few radicals in their midst who wanted to "throw off the British yoke." Yet they were patriots and their resolutions had weight both with the viceroy's legislative council and with the educated public.

Mohandas had never before attended a meeting of the congress. He found members and visitors settling themselves in a huge camp on the edge of Calcutta near the meeting hall. Of course, Gokhale always took a prominent part in the sessions and he was the first to welcome Gandhi.

He took his disciple under his wing, presented him to the leaders, and announced that Gandhi had an important resolution on the South African situation to present.

This was a happy initiation for Mohandas. Later, however, as he wandered alone about the camp, he was horrified by what he saw. Here among the most cultured, responsible, and eminent citizens appeared the very evils against which he had been fighting among the ignorant workers in South Africa.

First was apparent the absolute lack of unity in this so-called national body. Each geographical or religious or tribal group lived off by itself with its own kitchens and water supply. Mohammedans would not share their well with Hindus, and members from the far south were almost ostracized by proud descendants of the northern Kashmiri people.

Worst of all was the absolute lack of decent sanitary provisions. Not only was the camp absolutely filthy, but everyone was serenely indifferent to the appalling smells. In order to use the latrine in his own quarters, Gandhi borrowed a broom and a pail of water and scrubbed it for half an hour each day.

His efforts amazed, even shocked, all who saw him at work. "Why do you stoop to an Untouchable's job?" asked one man scornfully. To which Mohandas replied with a happy grin, "Because the Brahmins have made this an untouchable place."

As for the sessions, he found them disappointing. Only Gokhale and a few others lifted the meetings out of an atmosphere of jolly but frivolous sociability. Gandhi's resolution was swiftly passed, too swiftly for thorough consideration, he told Gokhale. The two men spent nearly a month together after the end of the session and enjoyed the frankest possible exchange of views.

"Naturally," said Mohandas one night at dinner, "I admire your efforts to push self-government for India. But how can you blame the English for believing we're not ready for it? Don't you think the caste system keeps members of the congress from getting together on an issue? As for our living habits . . . well! If this session of notables had lasted three days longer, a most fearful epidemic would certainly have broken out. Why would any Westerner think we are a civilized people?"

Gokhale listened with interest. "You have a special mission," said he, "for you see both sides of the case."

On his way across India to Bombay, Gandhi decided to pay his first visit to Benares. This is the most ancient and sacred city in the land. It is built along one bank of the Ganges River, which descends from the Himalaya Mountains, believed to be the snowy dwelling place of the three greatest Hindu gods.

Miles of stone steps line the bank of the wide river. If a Hindu bathes in the sacred Ganges, his earthly self is purified. If, after death, his body is burned on a pyre beside the waters, his soul makes a glorious entrance into its new life. Magnificent temples welcome the pilgrims bringing flowers and gifts to show their adoration. Some of these pilgrims are Hindus and others are followers of Buddha. For in Benares Budda taught his gospel of love and resignation.

Gandhi's mother had once been one of the pilgrims. As he entered the city one early morning, he thought of the way her face looked when she came back home from the holy city. It was like a plant washed clean by the rain, tender, serene, and strong.

He longed to share that experience. For a moment as he stood close to the river, he thought he might. For on the faces of the hundreds of bathers was a look of joyous purification which brought back his youthful awe. Yet the moment he mounted the steep steps to one of the golden-domed temples, he lost that sense of oneness with his fellow pilgrims. Flies buzzed everywhere. Vendors in stalls called out their wares and the loud chatter of crowds added to the hideous noise.

Even in the temple itself he could find no peace. Where was the spirit of devout meditation he had expected? Piles of rotted flowers near the sacred images greeted him with a sickening stench. The beautiful marble floors were dirty. Priests in gorgeous robes seemed intent only on collecting money and gifts from each pilgrim. Sadly Gandhi stood by the Well of Knowledge, most holy of the shrines. Not here in Benares could he ever find the God he so constantly sought.

On the way to the railway station he had no relief. In narrow, littered streets cows, regarded with veneration by all true Hindus, wandered at will. Borne by a hot breeze from the river bank, the smoke of funeral pyres stung his nostrils.

He almost laughed at himself to reflect that all this ugliness was but a curtain raiser for the scenes to come. For

he was traveling third-class. That had seemed to him the best way to learn about conditions which India's poorest people had to meet.

Pushed and shoved by chattering crowds on the railroad platform, he barely managed to scramble into a carriage. Its wooden benches were filled with old men, women, and children. With a group of younger men, Gandhi found just room enough to sit cross-legged on the floor. Foul odors in the packed, airless place were overpowering. So was the noise. Behind their veils Moslem women gossiped together in shrill dialect. Children wailed with hunger and discomfort. Bony old peasants in dirty loincloths and ragged shirts argued in harsh tones and spit on the floor the juice of the betel nuts they were chewing.

Gazing from one dark face to another, Gandhi felt at once depressed and compassionate. This was India—a neglected, ignorant, half-starved people! It hurt him to see how abashed, almost terrified, they were when the conductor stuck his head in the door. His shouted commands, his impatience with questions seemed in keeping with the railroad's indifference to the comfort of the passengers.

Gandhi's brother was shocked to learn that he had traveled third-class. But Mohandas answered, "If people of means and influence would sometimes go third-class, they'd see to it that conditions were made better."

It was in Bombay that Gandhi settled down with his family to practice law. Now he had time to learn something of the big city. In sharp contrast with the wide shore drives, the fine residences of English officials and Indian millionaires, the Gothic town hall, and the big hotels, were the native quarters and the bazaars. There he found the undiluted flavor of the East. Bazaar merchants sold everything imaginable. Incense and fried rice cakes, sandalwood and spices sent up a blend of odors at once revolting and romantic. Gandhi's heart was twisted by the incredible dirt and dire poverty. To see whole families sleeping and eating in the streets made him ashamed. Yet he was always ready to laugh at the antics of magicians and the majestic claims of rug sellers.

Mohandas had no more than started to build up his practice when a cable from South Africa disrupted all his plans. Because the colonial secretary from London was to visit Natal and the Transvaal, the Natal Indian Congress needed Gandhi to present its case to him. Gandhi had promised the leaders to return if it was considered necessary. Therefore Kasturbai and his brother argued in vain against his going. "I must keep my word," he said firmly.

He arrived in Durban in time for a conference with the English colonial secretary. Gandhi drew up and presented to that official a petition for relief from the grievances afflicting Indians in Natal. Immediately afterwards, at the request of his co-workers, he followed the secretary to Pretoria in order to perform the same service for Indians in the Transvaal. He agreed with the congress that to make a direct protest to a representative of the imperial government was essential. But, as he foresaw, it produced only a vague, halfhearted promise that the situation would be examined.

What made Gandhi glad he had returned was not this doomed attempt to get help from England. It was facing with his countrymen their crisis in the Transvaal.

His very first day in Pretoria showed Mohandas a city paralyzed by the recent war. Shops and banks were barely struggling back to life. Business and government offices were in a muddled state as the English took over. The dusty streets were full of soldiers. Sullen-looking black-bearded Boers wandered about. Many of them were farmers whose land had been turned into desert. They would have to borrow money for seed and tools to begin again.

In the midst of this confusion Indian traders and workers were trying to resettle themselves and their families. Most of them had fled from the Transvaal during the war. Now they found that they had to get permits to return, even to homes they owned outright. Worse still was the fact that the English who controlled the newly established Asiatic department made it exceedingly difficult to get these permits.

Mohandas had heard this much before he went one morning to visit the section in Pretoria where the Indians were compelled to live. Many of the huts were still deserted. In front of one of them stood an ox cart. With the help of a woman in a bedraggled sari a man was unloading boxes and furniture. Three small naked children sat on the ground watching them. Obviously they were all Untouchables. Staring as the well-dressed stranger walked up to them with a friendly smile, the man respectfully snatched off his turban.

But when Mohandas congratulated him on getting his permit to return home, he gave a groan. "I am a garbage collector, sir," said he, "and they say I can go back to work. But I had saved money to start a tool repair shop and now it's all gone. I had to pay it all out to the man who gave me the permit."

Bribery! Horrified by this revelation, Gandhi went about the whole day long collecting evidence. It was true. Either families had to wait for months to get back to the Transvaal or they had to pay huge fees for the privilege. That night he spent hours considering the plight of his countrymen. There was no one to guide them or protect them from ruin. The conclusion was plain. His duty was here after all and not in India. With his knowledge of law he could plead the cause of the poor. His decision to stay in South Africa was, he felt in a flash of intuition, the most important one he had ever made.

In the bustling town of Johannesburg, full of engineers and executives connected with the big gold mines, Gandhi settled down. Without trouble he was enrolled in the Supreme Court and at once went to work to break up the bribery system in the Asiatic department. He managed to get two officials brought to trial. Although an English jury acquitted them, the case was so notorious that the men were at once discharged, and the department heads put an end to bribery for good and all.

From then on clients came pouring in upon Gandhi. His earnings were huge. A large proportion of them were at once diverted to a new project. He had taken over a weekly paper called *Indian Opinion*, which he now published in both English and the language of his own home province. The journal served a double purpose. It presented to a British audience the truth about Indian difficulties and gave Indian readers a liberal education. With terrifying frankness he wrote about the evils of the caste system, the stupidity of prejudice between Mohammedans and Hindus, the crying need of home sanitation, and the wickedness of belief in Untouchability.

His own lack of prejudice against outcasts was suddenly dramatized for all to see. The black plague was brought to the Indian section of Johannesburg by twenty-three mine workers. The moment he heard of it Mohandas hurried to the spot. Already a brave doctor was there and soon a Scotch nurse appeared. With a few young Indian friends Gandhi helped improvise a hospital. He worked all the first night and for days devoted himself to the stricken community.

After a while Johannesburg's health officer came out. He said to Gandhi, "We are going to burn down this entire collection of huts to prevent spread of the plague. Please tell your people we are moving them to a tent colony outside the city and will provide all supplies. Get them to take it quietly, will you?"

Gravely Mohandas gazed at him. "If city officials had ever taught these poor ignorant people anything about sanitation or even supervised the district, you wouldn't have to do this. Now, of course, burning the huts is the best remedy. But I shall ask the town for compensation for each home owner."

The terrified Indians "took it quietly" because their friend told them to do so. But one thing troubled them terribly. "What about our savings?" they wailed. "We bury our money in the ground around our houses."

Cheerfully Mohandas told them to dig it up and bring

it to his office. He would take care of it for them. In order
to persuade the English bank to take the cash, he had to
guarantee to disinfect it. The tiny sums from each family
amounted to three hundred thousand dollars in coins. To
disinfect them, list each credit, and establish savings accounts was a stupendous job. Moreover, as the Indians
themselves well knew, Mohandas ran a second risk in
undertaking it. Since many patients and the brave nurse
had died of the infection, they marveled at Gandhi's
escape. "He is protected by God," they said.

It was shortly after this experience that Gandhi started a
new project. He decided that he was going to found a community where people could make brotherhood come true.
Near Durban he bought a farm of one hundred acres. Six
families started the colony and he moved the press and
publication office of *Indian Opinion* out there. The tiny village was named Phoenix. Gardens and handicrafts were
soon started, for all who joined the group believed in simple
living close to the earth.

By this time a year had passed and Gandhi was still sure
that his mission was in South Africa. Therefore he sent for
his family. With the exception of his eldest son, who remained at school in India, they all came. With them they
brought a young cousin devoted to Mohandas. Later several other young men whose fathers Gandhi had known
joined the group.

Gandhi was delighted with his household in Johannesburg and his gaiety infected everyone. Yet even the little
boys came to realize that he was engaged in some kind of
serious work all by himself. He set aside a definite period
for daily meditation. He was also learning by heart im-

portant parts of the great Hindu religious poem, the *Gita*. For this he had to use every possible scrap of spare time.

One morning his twelve-year-old son stopped in the doorway of the bathroom to gaze in astonishment at the figure before the washbowl. "Father," he cried, "what are you doing, mumbling to yourself? What is that paper pinned up there?"

A gay laugh floated into the hall. "I'm learning a great poem while I wash and brush my teeth. Why waste time? You might try the same thing, my boy."

Mohandas devoted great attention to the education of his three sons. He made lessons fun and walks in the country a means to learn accurate observation. He did not interfere with Kasturbai's physical care of the children. But he himself was making experiments with diet.

"I intend to be the ruler of my body," he said to the members of the household. "Its demands for pleasure interfere with progress. The spirit can only rule me if I am free of earthly wants."

Unprotesting, Kasturbai watched the list grow. Coffee and tea had long before been eliminated. Milk went next. Breakfast was reduced to a little gruel and fruit. Every now and then Mohandas ate nothing at all for twenty-four hours and found that by drinking water he had strength enough for the day's work.

Never did he preach such restraints to others. But the two young Englishmen whom he had invited to live in his house also tried out a few of these ideas. Kasturbai followed suit to some extent. Of course she had always shunned meat, and once when she was very ill she even refused to obey the doctor's order to take beef tea.

Several times during the course of his work Gandhi met Jan Smuts, one of the Boer leaders in the days of the republic. During the war against the British he had served as a dashing and brilliant general, and the moment it ended he threw himself into the work of restoring order. His ambition was to have the Boers share in the government of a united South Africa and he ably promoted the idea. Although Gandhi sympathized with this effort, he had reason to fear the tall blue-eyed General Smuts. For he was as much opposed to the presence of Indians in the Transvaal as any Englishman.

No matter how much respect and liking Gandhi won for himself during these years, he was never free of the knowledge that the white man's hatred threatened his countrymen. For this reason a sudden decision he had to make was painfully wrenched from him.

When he organized an ambulance corps for British service during the Boer War, he never dreamed that he would repeat the experience. Yet when the Zulus, a Negro tribe in the north, rebelled against the English, he again called for volunteers. Again many of his followers questioned the rightness of this move. Were not the Zulus upstanding men, good farmers, and brave warriors? And again Gandhi explained that only by supporting the English would the Indians ever gain freedom.

The instant his offer of help was accepted by the British commander, Gandhi moved his family down to the Phoenix colony. He and his twenty-four volunteers were given the welcome task of caring for the wounded Zulus whom no white man would touch.

Moving with the army, the men of the ambulance corps sometimes walked forty miles in a single day. This time Gandhi was far closer to the horrors of war than during the struggle with the Boers. As he strode along the paths winding around bare hills and down into valleys where Zulus had their primitive farms, the crackle of gunfire was ever in his ears.

Now, as never before, he faced the reality of men's mutual hatred. Unchecked, it would destroy the world. For years Mohandas had believed that every form of violence was wicked. In speeches and editorials he had said that men must learn how to win a just cause by love. During this man hunt in the wilderness his conviction blazed into passion. Of course, ruthless aggression, unjustified rebellions, and many other evils had to be fought. But without bloodshed, without hate! There must be some way to do battle in that fashion. Here in the wilderness Mohandas saw that to such a cause he could devote his whole life.

As he bathed the wounds of Negroes who had been shot or flogged, he longed to atone for the suffering inflicted upon them. Such tenderness flowed from his hands that often a Zulu, unable to communicate in words, would plant on his arm a sudden kiss of gratitude. Mohandas would silently pray that he might become worthy of his newly adopted cause. When the Zulu rebellion had been put down, he returned to Johannesburg fired with resolution.

To prepare himself, he set about living austerely, like one of the holy teachers so revered in India. The outward sign of his dedication was a series of editorials in *Indian Opinion* devoted to the idea of nonviolent struggle against oppression. The very first of them brought letters filled with eager interest. Humility, self-sacrifice, and reverence for all forms of life were familiar principles of Hindu and Buddhist teaching. From Indian subscribers came requests for more articles on this theme. In South Africa Indian leaders asked how such an idea could be used.

For them life was made increasingly hard. Successful traders had been driven out of the Orange Free State. In the Transvaal they had to have licenses, which could be revoked at the will of the administrator. Many indentured workers who would not renew five-year contracts and could not pay the poll tax were deported. Untouchables and manual laborers were made to live in special sections of Transvaal towns. "What new chains will they forge for us?" was the bitter question at every Indian gathering.

Soon came the answer. One August day in 1906 Gandhi was at his office in Johannesburg. Picking up the journal which published all official announcements, he saw that a new ordinance for Indians had been prepared. The moment he read the clauses he hurried with the journal to the office of a co-worker.

"Look here!" he cried, waving the paper. "This is too much to bear!"

The ordinance required all Indians—men, women, and children—to register for a personal certificate with name and thumb print. The card must be carried by the individual at all times and be shown on demand by police or trade inspectors. Anyone not able to produce his certificate could be fined, imprisoned, or deported.

Trembling with fury, Gandhi's friend cried, "Are we criminals, to be fingerprinted?"

"We must tell everyone about this ordinance at once," said Mohandas. "If it takes all night we'll translate it and print it in *Indian Opinion*."

Hardly was the journal issued when men began storming into Gandhi's office crying, "What can we do?" They were told a meeting was to be called to discuss that question.

Two weeks later a mammoth crowd jammed the old Empire Theater in Johannesburg. Delegates arrived from every corner of the Transvaal. The most striking feature of the gathering was that for the first time a number of women joined it. Husbands, fathers, and brothers had actually permitted them to come from behind the sheltering curtain of protection to face the issues with men.

From his seat on the platform Gandhi recognized farmers, law clerks, waiters, mine workers, and wealthy merchants. He observed in the front row several reporters from Johannesburg newspapers and watched them nudge one another with cynical grins as speaker after speaker shouted his despairing suggestions as to how this Black Act, as they called it, could be blocked. Many spoke of collecting weapons to resist by force. Others declared every Indian should leave South Africa.

At last Gandhi rose to his feet. He looked small and rather frail. The noisy, restless audience had become breathlessly still. Hundreds of eyes were fixed on him.

For an instant he simply looked into the distance. Then he spoke. "This ordinance is not one I can obey. I'd rather go to jail . . . even die."

"Yes, yes!" "We also!" People were on their feet, shouting.

One of the Mohammedan speakers on the platform

rushed forward. "I propose that we all take a solemn oath in the name of God never to submit to such a thing!"

Excitement rose higher. People were clapping, stamping, yelling. But as Gandhi lifted his hand, the confusion ceased.

"Let no one take this oath, this solemn oath, who is not able to keep it," said he. "I agree with our brother that such an ordinance cannot be obeyed by men of spirit. Yet you must understand the consequences of such a pledge. To break an oath taken in the name of God is a fatal deed."

The slow voice held everyone in a spell of quiet. It went on. "Our protest will come to nothing unless it is made in the right way. We must not resist police or troops who may try to force us to register. We shall probably have to go to prison, take blows and hard treatment. Perhaps we'll lose our property as punishment for disobedience. Let no one take this pledge who is not ready to suffer. Let no one take it who wishes to return blow for blow and hate for hate."

From all parts of the theater came cries. "We are ready!" "Lead us!" "Take our pledges!" "Allah be praised!"

The faces looking up at the platform were filled with joy. Here was a leader whom all could follow. They knew he had turned his back on all earthly rewards, used his huge earnings for the community, and lived as simply as any peasant. Such a man would ask nothing of them that he would not do himself.

Quietly everyone in the audience stood up. Every hand was raised. Slowly and clearly the vow was uttered in unison. "We swear in the name of the Everlasting God . . ."

In a solemn mood Gandhi left the theater. He had told

the members of the audience to talk to friends and workers in their communities and take their pledges to boycott the ordinance. Yet he feared too few really understood the guiding principle of effective revolt.

To his cousin, who helped him publish *Indian Opinion*, he said, "Those reporters at our meeting called our idea passive resistance. But it is really a very positive way of resisting. We must find a word for our principle of nonviolent action which all Indians will understand. Let's print in the journal the offer of a prize for the best term."

The offer stirred up wide interest. Suggestions came in by the dozens. It was Gandhi's cousin who won the prize. He combined two Indians words, *sat*, meaning truth, and *agraha*, meaning firmness. *Satyagraha* signifies that a man must declare the truth in which he believes and be willing to die for it without violence to anyone. Like a mighty flash of lightning the word *satyagraha* swept over South Africa. It struck fire in every Indian heart.

Meanwhile, meetings were held in towns and villages. Pledges of disobedience were made by the hundreds. In the midst of the excitement the ordinance was passed. But it was not to be enforced until the government of the Transvaal Crown Colony was formally organized. Gandhi and the men close to him hoped that the Black Act would then be repealed instead of enforced. For the political situation was swiftly changing.

In England new elections had put liberal men in Parliament and posts of power. They had always opposed their country's part in the Boer War and were eager to grant the defeated people a share in the government. Surely, thought

Mohandas, no liberal would approve an ordinance so brutally based on race prejudice.

At a conference of Indian leaders one of them said to Gandhi, "Bhai, you must go to London at once and present our cause to the new colonial secretary."

With a leader of the Mohammedan faith, Gandhi did take a hurried trip to London. But on his return he could report little encouraging news to the Indian Congress. "The men now in power have just as much prejudice against dark-skinned people as the conservatives."

In keeping with this grim pronouncement was the first legislation passed by the 1907 legislature. The Asiatic Registration Act did not oblige women to carry certificates. Otherwise it was an exact duplicate of the original ordinance. On July 31st it was to go into effect. During the spring and early summer Gandhi organized an association for resisting the act, and plans for doing so were drawn up.

Toward the end of July a final meeting was called. In the parklike grounds of a Mohammedan mosque in Pretoria thousands of Indians gathered. They sat cross-legged on the ground, packed so closely that they made a solid human floor. Gandhi was the only speaker. When everyone had arrived, he stood up and instantly silence fell.

Grave and quiet was the face bent down upon the crowd. Gandhi was praying for strength to lead these people into danger and suffering. Could they endure blows, injury to their families, and deep humiliation without a single act of revenge? Then he smiled. He was suddenly aware of deep springs of faith. His people would follow their ancient teachings of truth.

"We shall not obey this act," he said slowly and clearly. "We shall picket the places of registration and refuse to enter them. Let the government imprison and abuse us. No terms with this injustice shall be made. Violence will not stain our hands. For we are brave enough to disdain resistance. Be ready, friends. The hour for *satyagraha* has struck."

CHAPTER VII

FOR DAYS BEFORE AND AFTER THAT MEETING GANDHI'S
law office was headquarters for the Indian rebellion. His devoted Scotch secretary found herself interviewing little men
from India's far south and giants from the Pathan tribes
living in the northwest on the border of Afghanistan.

In all the messages sent flying here and there and in all
personal interviews Gandhi gave explicit plans. "Groups
will take turns walking quietly up and down in front of the
registration offices. Any Indian who approaches should be
told why we are refusing to register for the thumb-printed
certificates. If any picket is arrested, he must quietly go
to jail."

One morning at the office a former client of Gandhi's
listened carefully to his directions. He was Mir Alam, one
of the Pathan giants and a Mohammedan. "But suppose,"
he thundered, "some Indian will not refuse to register.

What do we do then?" As he spoke he threateningly doubled up his massive fist.

Gandhi leaned across the desk and laid his thin fingers on that fist. Looking into the wild dark eyes, he said in a tone of mock ferocity, "If any Indian wants to obey this unjust law, you must"—he paused to laugh gaily—"just sigh and let him go and be fingerprinted." Then in quite another tone he added firmly, "No violence, Mir Alam! Not against either the British or a fellow Indian. Otherwise the power of *satyagraha* is broken."

In August the protest started. All day in front of registration offices throughout the Transvaal marched constant processions of Indians in European clothes, Indians in white trousers and Parsi coats, Indians with hardly any clothes at all. Englishmen and Boers on their way to work almost fell off their bicycles to stare at the pickets. And well they might! Some thirteen thousand Indians were obliged by law to get certificates. Only five hundred and eleven men did so.

For weeks the government did nothing. Then one morning Gandhi's secretary greeted him with an excited outcry as he entered the office. "They are beginning to arrest the picketers!"

He received the news with anxious face. But as jails began to fill with those who refused to obey the law and as he assured himself that not a single case of resistance to the police was reported, his heart beat with triumph. Nor did this feeling waver when one December day he himself with twenty-four other leaders was brought before a magistrate.

As Mohandas looked about the room where he had so often defended his clients, he felt very strange indeed.

"Mr. Gandhi," barked the official, "as the one chiefly responsible for this lawlessness of your countrymen, you are commanded to leave the Transvaal."

"I understand, your Honor," replied Gandhi.

But he did not leave, and two weeks later he also was in jail. Although the cell was crowded and the food not of a kind an Indian could eat, Gandhi made no complaints, endured hideous discomfort, and spent hours reading the *Gita* and other religious books and studying the language of southern India. Meanwhile, study was becoming difficult because more and more prisoners were packed into the cell.

On the 30th of January, 1908, the jailer's key turned in the lock of the big room. Beckoning to Gandhi, the guard told him in a low tone that he was to be taken to Pretoria to see General Smuts. Smuts was now colonial secretary for the Transvaal. Under guard Mohandas made the journey and under guard was ushered into the office of the famous warrior. With a glance at the tall bearded man behind the desk, Gandhi said to himself as he had many times before, that the great Boer general looked more like a professor than a man of action.

Fixing keen blue eyes on the prisoner, Smuts said in slightly accented English, "This movement you have started, Gandhi, must stop at once. It is not in me to dislike Indians, but they must obey the laws on the statute books."

Quietly Mohandas replied, "It is a law meant to humiliate one single group of citizens, General. I would rather die than submit to it."

For some time the general continued to argue and Gandhi maintained his calm resistance. At last, however, they reached a compromise. Gandhi promised to end *satyagraha* on two conditions: first, that the Black Act be repealed, and, second, that all prisoners be released at once. On those terms he would urge his followers to register voluntarily pending the repeal of the Act. Heartily Smuts gave his word that he would release all political prisoners and, provided the Indians did register of their own accord, would insist that the legislature repeal the law. On this agreement they parted.

Even before he left Pretoria, Gandhi sent telegrams to all Indian leaders announcing that picketing should cease and that voluntary registration should begin. His return home was the signal for a deluge of visitors inquiring whether the change meant success or failure.

"It is a compromise," he explained. "We are not to be compelled by law to carry certificates and cannot be arrested for lack of them. If we show our good will by prompt registration, Secretary Smuts will see that the Black Act is repealed."

At this one of the visitors said in a frightened voice, "But have you heard? Mir Alam, the Pathan, has said he will strike dead the first man who follows your orders and goes to get his certificate."

Gandhi shook his head. "Mir Alam could not mean that. I shall be the first to register, for I am the man who made the compromise."

Next day Mohandas set out early to get his certificate. Suddenly a huge figure loomed up beside him and a harsh voice roared, "Where are you going?"

Gandhi's quick eye recognized Mir Alam. "To the registration office. You see . . ."

The sentence was unfinished. A terrific blow felled him to the street. There he lay unconscious. He was not aware that two passers-by rushed to help him, that several others seized his assailant, and that another man called the police. When Mohandas recovered his senses, he found himself on a couch in the office of an Englishman he barely knew. In a flash the scene of the attack came before him.

Struggling to sit up, he said weakly, "Do not blame Mir Alam! He did not understand." Next he insisted that a clerk from the registration office come to take his fingerprints and make out his certificate. "I promised to be the first to register," he explained to the protesting group around him.

When his wounds were bound up and his heart had regained its regular beat, he sent for his secretary. The shocked girl had to take down his statement for *Indian Opinion* and the English press. He begged the authorities to take no action against the fierce Pathan and asked his followers to forgive the man who had struck him down. "Let no Hindu feel hurt," he said, "because the attack was by a Mohammedan."

As she closed her notebook, the Scotch girl said, "You are truly a great soul, Mr. Gandhi."

That was what Indians in South Africa were beginning to call him. *Mahatma*, or Great Soul, is the Indian title for a man whose spiritual life is of such purity that his very presence brings a blessing. Even when, like the Pathan giant, people did not fully understand his motives, they were ready to do as he said. Slowly, as the volunteers drifted in, registration clerks issued certificates to the Indian population. All prisoners had been released and no further arrests were made among those who did not register promptly.

On one of his frequent trips down to Phoenix to see his family, Mohandas said to his son, "We Indians have now fulfilled our part of the compromise. When the legislature meets, it will be General Smuts' turn to act."

The boy was now about seventeen, an upstanding fellow who was deeply interested in the struggle his father was making for Indian justice. "Suppose," he said thoughtfully, "Smuts does not keep his promise. Suppose he doesn't ask for the repeal of the Black Act. What will you do then?"

"We shall start another general protest," said Gandhi.

These events followed one after another. Smuts sent no word about the registration bill to the legislature. Gandhi started another *satyagraha* and on October 15th, 1908, he joined hundreds of his followers who had been sent to jail. Among them was his son. First Gandhi was imprisoned in Johannesburg and then transferred to the Pretoria jail. He divided his time between battling for better food for his companions and continuing his studies. At last, on the 15th of December, he was released.

Immediately he called a conference of Hindu and Mohammedan leaders. Everyone realized that the battle for Indian justice had just begun. Spirits were high. Since so many thousands of workers had taken part in the protest, *satyagraha* as a political weapon had proved its worth.

One of the leaders had already thought out the next move. "Bhai," he said to Gandhi, using the affectionate word meaning brother, "it is certain that the English officials in London are told nothing of our situation here. We want you to go to London and speak to the colonial secretary about our cause."

Such a trip meant both expense and a serious interruption to his law work. Yet Gandhi agreed to go. To his delight one of his new friends decided to go with him. This man was a successful architect, a German who owned a good deal of land near Johannesburg. He had become deeply interested in all Gandhi's ideas, from experiments in diet to the founding of the Phoenix colony. Together they stopped there on the way to board their ship for England.

More people had now joined the colony and it was a thriving place. Everyone, including Kasturbai and the children, seemed happily engaged in work and in the peaceful life of the community. The architect was so impressed with all he saw that as soon as they were comfortably settled on the boat, he made a surprising proposal.

"Why not start another colony near Johannesburg, my friend? I'll lend you my big farm and it's good land. It could serve as a haven for all your people who have lost jobs and homes because of their protests against these unfriendly laws."

For hours the two men planned the project. Gandhi was so happy about this new design for aid to his followers that he could bear calmly the utter failure of the English visit. Although he was allowed to address a group of one hundred members of Parliament, he was unable to draw from them any promise to redress Indian grievances.

The year 1910 saw the beginning of the new colony. Gandhi named it Tolstoy Farm in honor of the great Russian novelist whose ideas of simple living had deeply influenced him. This community, even more clearly than Phoenix, proved that Hindus and Mohammedans, Untouchables and Brahmins could live and work together.

Gandhi persuaded the children to share religious ceremonies. Mohammedan youngsters delighted in the Hindu festival of light when tiny lamps glowed in the windows of every Hindu hut. Hindu children shared part of the greatest Mohammedan fast. Then they prepared for their Mohammedan playmates a feast of cakes and sweetmeats to enjoy when the fast had ended.

Gandhi spent as much time as possible at the farm. He taught the children in the school and tried to make their farm chores seem like fun. Although he always laughed at their pranks, he won their complete loyalty to his gentle authority.

In 1910 the dream of Boer leaders came true. The South African Union became a fact. Its capital was in Pretoria and the legislature met in Capetown. Glad as he was that the British had allowed the Boers self-government within the empire, Gandhi bemoaned one result of it. Jan Smuts was at once appointed Minister of the Interior, Mines, and Defense. This put at the head of Indian affairs a man of proved hostility to Indians.

In vain during the next two years Gandhi tried to win from Smuts a just attitude toward the Indian population. In vain he directly petitioned the legislature to repeal the Black Act and the poll tax which kept indentured Indians enslaved. Reports of the failure of all these efforts were constantly sent to Gopal Gokhale. In turn he did much to

arouse all the organizations and the leaders in India. Finally
he himself arrived in South Africa to make his own appeal
to the Union government.

For Gandhi this visit was a dazzling series of events.
Gokhale had tremendous prestige with the English. From
the moment Mohandas met him at Capetown, he was
caught up in the whirl of entertainments given his distinguished friend by all the liberal thinkers in that city.
From interviews with leading men in the legislature Gokhale came away very hopeful of securing relief legislation.
Then on to Johannesburg went the two men and during the
journey they had ample opportunity to talk over all their
problems.

To the delight of all his compatriots, Gokhale was given
a royal welcome by Johannesburg's mayor. Finally at a dinner for the visitor organized by four hundred leading Indians came the climax. Gokhale announced in triumph that
he had received promises from the prime minister of the
Union and from even Jan Smuts himself that reforms
would be undertaken and that the poll tax on indentured
servants would be repealed.

Almost as satisfying to Gandhi as this thrilling announcement was Gokhale's enthusiasm for Tolstoy Farm. He
spent three days at the colony and was plainly reluctant
to leave.

"You cannot imagine," said he to Mohandas at parting,
"how glad I have been to see this experiment with my own
eyes. We've heard so much about it in India and now I can
report every detail. Nothing like this community of races,
faiths, and castes has ever been known in the world before.

In fact, my friend, your work in South Africa has taught us much."

Gokhale's visit had inspired great hopes. But they were short-lived. When the legislature met early in 1913, Smuts refused to ask for repeal of the poll tax. He declared he could not go against the opposition of mine owners and industrialists.

There was worse to come. By a decision made in March of that year, the Capetown Supreme Court announced a ruling which struck at the very foundation of Indian life. It stated that all marriages not celebrated by Christian rites were illegal. This meant that Hindu and Mohammedan wives were not wives at all and that their children had no standing in the community or in the courts of law.

In Pretoria, Johannesburg, and Durban, in Phoenix and at the Tolstoy Farm, Indians were in a white heat of fury. Every family, high and low, was affected by this court decision. Now for the first time women insisted on joining actively in protesting the judgment.

"Our honor and security have been destroyed!" they cried. "We have a right to protest. Let the government put us in prison! Already they have done something far worse to us."

Day and night Gandhi interviewed leaders and planned the campaign. This time the demonstration was to be on a grand scale. "Our strategy," said he, "is to break some unimportant regulation as an act of defiance toward an unjust government."

He accepted the offer of eleven women at Tolstoy Farm to serve as sacrificial pioneers. They were to disobey a regulation by crossing into Natal without permits. As they gathered about Mohandas to get his directions, they made a picturesque group in their bright cotton saris. In the glow of their dark eyes he read a determination he could entirely trust. "God bless you, my sisters!" he said.

Hastily arranging affairs in his office, he was just about to set off to Phoenix when his secretary brought him a telegram. It was from the eleven women. They reported that the border police had let them through without question. What should they do now? He wired back that they should proceed to the mining town of Newcastle and talk to the laborers there about the whole situation facing Indians. Already he had cabled Gokhale concerning the crisis and received back a question. "How many volunteers for *satyagraha* are you sure will take the risk?"

At Phoenix he found both men and women ready to undertake any and all risks. While he was talking to a group of them, Kasturbai hurried into the room. "What is the matter with me?" she asked her husband with flashing eyes. "Why am I unworthy to make a sacrifice to truth and justice? You have not counted me as one willing to go to jail."

First in surprise, then in admiration, Mohandas regarded his wife. "I had not thought of dragging you into this," he said in a tone of tender warmth, "but if it is your will to join *satyagraha*, I am happy."

Sixteen people from Phoenix were to march across the border into the Transvaal without permits. With Gandhi's ardent blessing they started. He hurriedly began to arrange for the continued publication of *Indian Opinion* in his absence.

At Durban he had word that the Tolstoy Farm women were convincing hundreds of miners that they must join the struggle. Next came news that the sixteen women from Phoenix, including Kasturbai, were in jail. Immediately afterwards Gandhi learned that the women agitators at Newcastle had been arrested and that in deep anger for such humiliation of women, hundreds of men had gone on strike. Newspapers reported that work at the mines had been brought to a standstill. To force the miners to return to work, the owners had cut off both water and light from the company-owned huts in which the workers and their families lived.

Dropping everything, Gandhi rushed off to Newcastle. He feared that the angry men might commit some act of violence. Somehow the miners got word of his coming. When he reached their community he was welcomed as no prince was ever greeted by a loyal people. Before he talked to them, however, he interviewed a group of mine superintendents and owners. They contemptuously refused to consider supporting a repeal of the poll tax. Having warned them politely that he intended to do battle, he called a meeting of all the strikers.

Sitting on the rough ground in the open air, the dirty, half-starved men looked up at him with touching eagerness. In his high clear voice he told them his plan. He had framed it in desperation. For he had to have some way of providing shelter and food for these helpless hordes. If the government arrested them, it would have to support them.

"We are going to march peaceably together across the border of the Transvaal. You know that is forbidden. The

government will certainly arrest us. This is a nonviolent way
of protesting the poll tax, the decision that our marriages
are illegal, and all the other laws drawn up against us. We
will show everyone that we are men, that we can sacrifice
ourselves for a just cause. And without harming anyone!
Are you ready to face arrest and harsh treatment without
striking a single blow?"

Roars of assent answered him. The miners were ready to
follow him anywhere. As soon as he could arrange to get
help from volunteers and money for supplies from rich Indian merchants, he gave the signal. Then the amazing
trek began.

Out of the mine district, out of the town, trudged more
than two thousand men, over a hundred women, and some
fifty children. The volunteer workers helped direct the long
lines of marchers. As they tramped along the dusty trails
circling the low mountains and crossing the harsh, unfriendly plains, men and women sang fragments of ancient
hymns. The procession had the air of a sacred pilgrimage.
No one was afraid.

Gandhi enjoyed the business of making camps. He himself stirred soup in big cauldrons. Carefully he and the volunteers showed the men how to dig latrines, dispose of
waste, and keep clean with the little water available. The
grateful response made to these first lessons in sanitation
delighted the leaders.

On the second evening the peaceful army reached a town
on the very border of the Transvaal. Lying on the ground
under the close splendor of the stars, Gandhi prayed for
strength to carry his great responsibilities. At dawn he wrote

a letter addressed to the government of the South African Union explaining why he had undertaken the expedition. He suggested that it might be well to arrest everyone then and there.

The message was dispatched. All day Gandhi waited for an answer. All day more thousands of strikers joined the crowd. They brought the news that in Natal twenty thousand more Indians were on strike.

Late that evening Gandhi roused from sleep to find himself confronted by several uniformed men. "You have come to arrest me, I know," he said quietly. To several of his helpers who had hurried to gather around him he gave last directions. Then he said, "I am ready to go with you, gentlemen."

Next morning, just as news of his arrest was spreading panic through the camp, Gandhi returned. Unable to find a legal excuse to hold him, the magistrate of the town had released him on bail.

On went the march. The border was crossed. For one more day the pilgrims were left in peace. Then the government struck. Gandhi and his volunteers were arrested. Trains rolled up filled with guards who drove the miners into cars to be taken back to Newcastle.

In his cell Gandhi learned that the laborers endured every hardship without protest. They were kept in barbed-wire enclosures at the mines, flogged, fed starvation rations. Yet they refused to work.

Three times during that month of November Gandhi was released from jail, rearrested, and sent to another jail. But nothing could daunt him now. *Satyagraha* had succeeded beyond his hopes. For it was not only in South Africa that Indians had been aroused to white heat. India itself was now identified with the struggle. Public meetings, petitions, and blazing newspaper headlines at last moved even the viceroy to action. He sent word to London that something must be done. In England liberal voices were raised in indignant protest.

By this time *satyagraha* had spread all through Natal and the Transvaal. Prisons were overflowing. Business men and government officials were at their wits' end. Pressed from all sides, General Smuts, Minister of the Interior, was obliged to act. He dodged the issue by appointing a commission of three to study the situation. Then he was obliged to receive two distinguished visitors from India who came on a mission of peace. One of them was an Englishman, Mr. Charles F. Andrews, teacher and writer, close friend of Gokhale, and staff member of the most famous school in India, founded by the great poet Rabindranath Tagore.

From time to time this news seeped in to the prison cell of the small brown man who had stirred up all this excitement on two continents and in the British Isles. He was contentedly reading what books the jailer allowed and going on with his study of the language of India's southern provinces.

In December, 1913, Gandhi was released. His joy at meeting Andrews was only matched by the deep interest Andrews took in him. Almost instantly the two knew one another as men of the same ideals and of equal love for India. From then on they were fast friends.

"Smuts is in a ghastly dilemma," said Andrews gleefully.

"He wants to make peace but thinks to yield is to admit defeat. The commission, however, will solve the matter. They will ask for immediate reform of anti-Indian legislation."

When Andrews and his companion departed for India, Gandhi sent General Smuts a politely haughty threat. If action were not taken on the Indian situation, he would start another march of workers.

That march never took place. For just then English and Boer railroad employees, taking advantage of the general confusion, called a great strike for an increase in wages. They expected support from the Indians. Together the two groups could have paralyzed the country. But instantly Gandhi commanded every Indian to go back to his job, at least temporarily.

"A fight for better wages," he explained to his workers and to the public, "must not be confused with our battle for human rights. Why should we wish to cripple the South African Union? All we want from it is simple justice."

That decision won the day for the Indians. Gratitude for Gandhi's fairness and friendliness swung public opinion to his side. The commission of investigation reported in favor of granting all the essential reforms demanded by Indian leaders. An Indian relief bill was therefore rushed through the legislature and signed by the royal governor. It abolished the poll tax on indentured workers, declared absolutely legal all marriages held legal in India, and removed penalties for crossing from one state into another.

The effect of this outcome was prodigious. A struggle of such huge proportions carried on without violence or resistance on the part of the strugglers had never been known in the world before. Stories of Gandhi's leadership and of his triumph over the combined power of English and Boers were published in many countries. In India every educated citizen, every man who had worked for political freedom exulted in the South African victory.

Gopal Gokhale's way of acknowledging the greatness of his political son was to send him a momentous request. He asked Gandhi to meet him in London that summer and join him in presenting to parliament and the colonial secretary plans for self-government in India.

Gandhi was electrified. Well he knew that acceptance of the invitation meant a clean break in his life, a shift of exertion back to India.

Was this his duty? After long reflection he realized that his work in South Africa had come to a natural end. During the last year the Tolstoy Farm colony had closed. But most of its residents had moved to Phoenix and that colony was thriving beyond need of special supervision. Strong leadership had developed among both Mohammedans and Hindus and they were working together in complete harmony. Since public sympathy had now been aroused in the Indian cause, problems could gradually be solved. Yes, he was free now to start out on a new path.

Joyously he announced his decision to Kasturbai. "You are going with me to London," he said. "From England we will return to India and the boys can join us there. The time has come to serve the people in our native land and you will help me, my brave girl, just as you have here."

Kasturbai turned upon him a happy smile. In newspaper

articles and speeches made at dinners of celebration she had been called over and over again "the heroine of South Africa." She had won her place and it was no longer in the background of her husband's life. Now she stood beside him, a partner in danger and suffering, with steady feet planted on the path of truth.

CHAPTER VIII

ONE JANUARY NIGHT IN 1915 AN ENGLISH STEAMSHIP crept stealthily toward the Bay of Bengal. Not a single light shone from portholes or captain's bridge. The sailors on duty slipped like dark shadows along the silent decks. Lookouts posted fore and aft took sweeping surveys through binoculars across the sea. Even in those waters so remote from Europe a ship was not entirely safe from the threat of submarine and raider. For this was the fifth month of the First World War.

In one of the darkened cabins the ship's doctor, flashlight in hand, was bending over a quiet figure in the berth. "Mr. Gandhi," said the doctor, "I stopped in to find out how you are tonight. Do you still feel pain in your lungs?"

Through the dimness Gandhi's voice had a hollow sound. "Thank you, doctor. I have only a very little pain now. Already I think the warmer air of the south is helping my pleurisy."

"Good night then. Sleep well. We'll doubtless land tomorrow noon."

When the door closed on the doctor's heels, Mohandas

lay very still and extremely busy. This last night on shipboard was his chosen time to review the experiences of the
last months.

First had come the shock of the news hurled at him a
few days after he landed in England from South Africa.
The German army had marched into Belgium, and England had declared war on the Kaiser. Of course this catas-
trophe smashed all plans for a conference on Indian affairs.
Moreover, Gokhale was stranded in Paris.

Immediately Gandhi threw himself into war work. He
began to organize a volunteer ambulance corps among Indians living in London and took a six-week first-aid
course. Just as he was ready for service, a severe attack of
pleurisy struck him down. It proved so stubborn that long
weeks passed before he was able to follow the London phy-
sician's advice to return to the warm climate of India.

It had been a bitter disappointment. However, Gandhi
turned on his pillow and deliberately began to recall his
happy moments in London. They began with the great dinner of welcome given him on his arrival. He would never
get over his amazement at the letters he received from the
prime minister and members of the cabinet. Many distinguished Indians seemed to be in London at that time
and, little by little, he met all of them. By far the most
colorful was Mrs. Sarajini Naidu. She was a wealthy Brahmin and a poet of renown. Very modern in her manner
and ideas, she had become an active worker for India.

In the dark Mohandas chuckled softly to remember their
meeting. She had burst into the little flat he and Kasturbai
had rented. It was five o'clock and he was sitting on the

floor eating his supper, with half a dozen little dishes of vegetables and fruit around him. How merry Mrs. Naidu was and what an exciting talk they had! As she left she said, "Gokhale said I must look you up and of course I couldn't wait to clap my little laurel wreath on the brow of our South African hero."

He spared a moment to wonder where Mrs. Naidu might be now. Then he went on to the future. Tomorrow, after twelve years' absence, he would be home again. What work awaited him in India? Surely his experience in South Africa would fit him better for some sort of service to his country.

Next day, dressed in a dhoti, long shirt, and a cloak woven of native Indian wool, Mohandas went slowly down the gangplank to the dock. Kasturbai was behind him. Suddenly he paused as a roar of voices rose from the wharf. Looking down, he saw a mass of people. They were waving and shouting, "Gandhi! Gandhi! Welcome, Gandhi!"

What did this mean? In bewilderment he found himself surrounded by a mass of people almost hysterical with joy. All at once the crowd divided and he saw Gokhale and the friend who was to entertain him at Bombay hurry forward. Hardly stopping to greet the newcomers, the two men pushed Mohandas and Kasturbai through the press and into a little carriage called a tonga.

As the horse started off, Gandhi gasped, "But how did so many people know of me?"

His host laughed. "What? Not know the man who led five thousand miners to a peaceful victory? Why, Gandhiji, you are a byword in India!"

Gandhiji! Mohandas smiled at this name, a cordial way

of saying Mr. Gandhi. The very sound of it made him feel at home again.

Hardly had the party been comfortably settled in the big house with its gardens front and back, when a note was delivered for Gandhi. It was from the English governor of the district, asking him to come for an interview.

"Now," laughed the host, "will you believe that your activities are known here? British officials are already afraid of you."

There was, however, no air of uneasiness in the governor's manner. Cordially receiving his visitor in a luxuriously furnished room of the official mansion, he waved him to a seat on the opposite side of the carved teakwood desk.

"Now that you are back in India, Mr. Gandhi," said the governor, "I should like you to make me a promise, one in keeping with your reputation for fair play."

Receiving a friendly nod from Gandhi, he went on. "Should you ever want to take action in the affairs of this province—the kind of thing you pulled off in South Africa— I want you to come and see me beforehand."

Promptly Mohandas replied, "Your Excellency, I need not even make the promise. It is my custom to warn an adversary in advance of taking any action. I always hope action may be avoided."

After a week of receiving visitors and attending receptions, Gandhi followed Gokhale to Poona, a town not far from Bombay. In spite of meetings large and small, the two friends managed a number of intimate talks. During these exchanges Mohandas was shocked by his friend's look of deathly illness and disconcerted by the change in his point of view.

"I no longer believe the British plan to give us self-government," Gokhale announced abruptly. "They'll never do it of their own free will. To them we are an inferior people whose happy fate is to serve the majestic British Empire and make it rich."

Thereupon he cited the much-advertised reforms of 1909. These measures allowed only a few men of education and wealth to vote. The Indians they elected to office had no power except to advise the British. Moreover, the government tried by fanning jealousy between Mohammedans and Hindus to prevent their working together for freedom.

Sadly Gandhi listened to these words from the man whose faith in England had once matched his own. But he himself had as yet no political experience in India. His mind was fixed on an idea which he straightway unfolded. He wanted to start in India a colony like Tolstoy Farm. Already a number of his best workers had returned from Phoenix to India and were staying at the famous school of arts founded by the great Indian poet, Rabindranath Tagore.

"Just as soon as we can find a suitable place for the colony," he concluded, "my family and I will combine with these people."

The tired eyes of the sick man lighted. "Excellent! You couldn't do anything better for India. To rush into reforms now would be folly. Far better to find out for yourself first what conditions really are." Then, with a return of his first bitterness, he added, "Not that it will make you like England any more to see our starving peasants bowed down by their high rents."

Gandhi's cherished talks with Gokhale at Poona were the last he was to enjoy. Just two weeks later he received news of his beloved friend's death.

After visiting relatives, Mohandas crossed India by slow train to Calcutta and on to Tagore's school. His first impression of the place was of red sandstone pavilions rising out of the dusty plain against a background of forest. Dozens of white-clad boys and girls strolled around the compounds. As he stepped out of the carriage which had brought him from the station, he was caught up in greetings from his devoted co-workers of Phoenix days. His new friend, Charles Andrews, was there to welcome him also.

It was a happy reunion. In the midst of laughter and talk someone murmured, "Ah, here comes the teacher!"

It was the first time Gandhi had ever seen the poet Rabindranath Tagore, whose works were read almost as eagerly in England and America as in his native land. Now, looking with profound interest at the tall robed figure and the noble face framed in long locks and flowing beard, he thought he had never been in such a majestic presence. Tagore's greeting to Gandhi fitted into this picture. Graciously he assured Gandhi that his group was welcome to stay at the school until a site for his own colony had been selected.

For weeks the Gandhis traveled back and forth across the country, attending meetings and visiting friends. Everywhere Mohandas went, his fame as a leader had preceded him. Nowadays he was hearing on all sides the title by which the South African Indians had addressed him. He was the Mahatma, Great Soul, whose presence brought blessing.

Such admiration proved a trial to Gandhi. He and his Phoenix group were invited to attend a great religious festival. Delightedly he undertook with the others the making of a clean, sanitary camp which was to be a shining example amid the general filth. But on the second morning while he was happily digging a trench for a latrine, his cousin hurried to take the spade from his hand.

"You cannot do this, Gandhiji," he said. "A crowd is waiting before your tent to get your blessing."

Over Gandhi's face stole a rebellious look, and after sitting for hours while crowds knelt before him he was utterly worn out. "I'd far rather have been using my spade," he told his cousin with a rueful laugh. Yet he understood why he was being persecuted with homage. Indians must offer it to any man who, they believe, is living by the ancient ideals of love and self-sacrifice.

Late in May, 1915, Gandhi's colony was launched. He had chosen a spot near Ahmedabad, a textile manufacturing town in his own part of the country. One of his friends had offered him a large bungalow as a beginning of the tiny village. Twenty-five men and women, all bound by vows of simple living and human service, gathered there and began to build their huts of mud and bamboo. They started a common garden and set up a community kitchen.

One day Gandhi called everyone together to hear news. He had had an application to join the group from an Untouchable family, man, wife, and little girl. The man had been a teacher and all were devout Hindus. Although Gandhi welcomed such a chance to show Indian leaders his defiance of the caste system, he did not press the colonists to agree to have them come. However, they all did agree. Even so, Kasturbai and the other women were a bit apprehensive about working in the kitchen with an Untouchable.

A few days after the quiet, pleasant trio of Untouchables arrived, a storm broke over the place. News of their acceptance in the colony had spread among all the strict Hindus in Ahmedabad. In horror they announced that neither they nor any other subscribers could continue to supply funds.

"What are we going to do now, Gandhiji?" asked his cousin, who was managing the funds. "We have hardly enough money to last a week."

Mohandas took the situation calmly. After reflection he said with laughter in his voice, "Doubtless we shall all have to become Untouchables. We'll move to the quarters set aside for them in Ahmedabad and earn our living by doing manual work."

"Of course," murmured Kasturbai hopefully, "you wouldn't think of asking the new family to leave?"

Her husband glanced at her pityingly. "Certainly not. It would wreck our whole purpose to go against our principles. They have to be practiced, not just announced."

Two days later Mohandas was just about to set off for town to inquire about room in the Untouchable quarter when a visitor arrived. As Gandhi stepped out on the veranda, he saw a shiny motor car drawn up in front of the bungalow. A swarthy man with a Mohammedan's turban wound about his head was waiting to speak to him.

Hastily returning Gandhi's courteous greeting, he said,

"I should like to help your community. Would you accept help from a Mohammedan?"

"Most certainly," replied Mohandas in astonishment.

With a word of thanks and a bow, the man jumped into his car and drove away. Next day he returned. Out of the car he dragged a huge canvas bag, staggered with it to the bungalow, and hurried away. In the bag were enough rupees from the nameless benefactor to pay all the expenses of the community for two years.

"Lord Krishna be praised!" everyone murmured in awed tones. It seemed to them a miraculous salvation.

This incident and the presence of Untouchables in the colony were discussed by Hindus up and down the land. But, although curiosity about Gandhi increased, there was small satisfaction for it that year. Mohandas stayed quietly in the Ashram, as the colony was called, meditating and teaching his helpers to work and live together in harmony. It was not until February, 1916, that he broke his silence. He was invited to speak at a great occasion held in the place dearest to the heart of India. The new University of Benares was being dedicated.

At that time only a few plain structures housed the university which today has a vast collection of modern buildings. Money for its founding had been given by public subscriptions, by Indian princes, and by the British government. Therefore the dedication had drawn notables of every description to Benares—the viceroy, English and Indian officials, officers in brilliant uniforms, famous professors in gowns with bright hoods, wealthy merchants, and students. Most resplendent of all were the maharajas or princes, garbed in embroidered costumes and laden with priceless jewels. All the speeches were in English, and over the splendid scene hovered an air of mutual good will. No one would have dreamed that on the western edge of Europe a terrible war was bringing death and destruction to humanity.

It was on the second day of the celebration that Gandhi made his first important public address in India. As he mounted the platform, the audience craned forward to gaze at the individual of whom they had heard so much. Was this the Mahatma? Before them stood a wisp of a man in cotton clothes, a man with thinning hair and ears like little wings flying out from his head. But his very first words froze the listeners to startled attention.

"It is a matter of deep humiliation and shame for me that I am compelled this evening, under the shadow of a great college in this sacred city, to address my countrymen in a language that is foreign to me."

The university professors stiffened. All their courses were to be given in English because of government patronage. British officials frowned in anger.

Gandhi explained that Indians were always criticized for being indifferent to progress. The fault was not going to be corrected if students had to spend their best years mastering a foreign tongue. After dealing with the question of language he next turned his guns on the princes. Reminding the audience that on the previous day the maharaja who presided had bemoaned India's poverty, he said his pity did not accord with the ceremonial pageant and the gorgeous show of jewels.

"I compare with the richly bedecked noblemen the countless numbers of the poor," he cried. "And I feel like saying to these noblemen, 'There is no salvation for India unless you strip yourselves of this jewelry and hold it in trust for your countrymen.' "

He added that Indians in high places should change their ways. Maharajas should have the filthy streets in their districts cleaned. Priests should clean the holy temples. High-caste Hindus should be gentle in their treatment of people less well born, especially on railway trains. "No amount of fair speeches will ever make us fit for self-government. It is only our conduct which will fit us for it."

Electrified, people sat forward on their seats. Some were purple with rage. Others looked transported with elation. On went the slow, clear voice to attack a matter so serious that it had been kept out of all newspapers in the country. Groups of students and young townsmen had formed terrorist clubs to show their hatred of English rule by violent acts. Bombs had been thrown. British officials had been assassinated. Such things could not be mentioned. India must be presented to all the world as a happy and loyal colony. But Gandhi attacked such acts in this public speech. He declared that they were the terrible deeds of misguided youths who must learn that they were only doing their own country the greatest possible harm.

Finally Gandhi, who had three times supported British war efforts, made the most astounding statement ever uttered in the land. "If I found it necessary for the salvation of India that the English should retire, that they should be driven out, I would not hesitate to declare that they would have to go, and I hope I would be prepared to die in defense of that belief."

When they had recovered from the shock, some of his listeners realized that beneath the stark words there was not a tinge of hatred for anyone. This man wanted only to purge India of its sins as he had purged himself of all worldly and physical desires. "Yes," they admitted, "it is no wonder that people call this little man Mahatma."

Although both Gokhale and he had agreed that it was better not to press for reforms immediately, Gandhi could never forget the plight of indentured workers. For this reason, those unfortunate men, forced or persuaded to leave India on the terms of a five-year contract at starvation wages, became the objects of his first great crusade. Backed by the added fame of his speech at Benares, he now began direct action. He interviewed leaders, made a few speeches, and wrote numerous articles. When thousands of people offered to support him, he resolved to interview the viceroy.

The English capital was now at New Delhi. This official city, an adjunct of the ancient town of Delhi, lies in the north-central part of India near the desert. Newly built stone mansions, parks, and boulevards combined with armed guards in glittering uniforms to make every visitor feel all the might and pomp of the British Empire. Some of these guards stood at the entrance to the viceroy's headquarters, and as Gandhi passed between them he smiled at the reflection of himself in those stony eyes. They were wondering how this humble visitor in a dhoti and with sandaled bare feet ever got a pass to their august viceroy.

The interview was brief. The viceroy listened attentively

while Gandhi set forth his case. So courteous and so gentle was the visitor's voice that England's representative took no offense even when Gandhi announced boldly that he meant to start an active campaign against the indentured labor system. It was on the viceroy's promise that he would do all in his power to help that Mohandas left.

The year 1916 closed with a meeting of the Indian Congress, which Gandhi attended. True, he expected nothing from those dreary sessions of talk which such meetings usually meant. Still, it was important to discuss his campaign with members. Especially did he look forward to meeting Motilal Nehru.

Nehru was a Brahmin whose aristocratic Kashmiri ancestors had stamped him with the fine features of an old Roman. He had made a fortune from his law practice and, although he was one who believed most firmly in the wisdom of working within the framework of English order, he was always sympathetic with his less fortunate countrymen.

Upon meeting Gandhi he expressed the liveliest interest in all that had been done in South Africa. The two men were still talking of those events when a younger man approached them. Strikingly handsome in feature, he was attired in striped trousers, cutaway coat, and patent-leather shoes.

"Ah, Gandhiji," said Motilal, "I should like to introduce to you my son Jawaharlal."

Gandhi looked up into dark eyes, both somber and glowing. Quickly he divined in them a spirit of greater rebellion against old forms and methods than the older Nehru had ever shown. At once he felt that this young man, freshly

graduated from the great English University of Cambridge, was an impassioned nationalist who would stop at nothing to right the wrongs against his country.

On the same afternoon Gandhi met another man who was to play a part in his life. As he was resting a few moments in his tent, a stocky figure appeared at the opening and a voice quivering with emotion cried, "Mahatma Gandhi, I must speak to you about our sufferings in the indigo fields of Bihar."

Gandhi sat up in surprise. The man was a decently dressed peasant. When, on Gandhi's invitation, he entered the tent, he began to pour out his woes. He was an indigo worker in the northern district of Bihar and, like all his fellows, was the victim of a villainous system. Part of the land which he rented had to be planted in indigo for the use of the landlord. He received no pay for this work. Although he could plant foodstuffs in the rest of his land, the yield was too small to pay the rent and support his family. Hounded by rent collectors, beaten and abused by landlords, the hard-worked indigo laborers were obliged to live almost like animals.

"Something must be done for us! Come and see, Mahatma Gandhi! Come and help us! Come at once."

Never before had Mohandas heard of indigo cultivation in India. He was moved by the peasant's impassioned plea and said that, busy as he was on a special campaign, he would go up to Bihar as soon as he could.

After the close of the congress session, Gandhi stopped at another town and there on the platform stood the peasant. Again he rushed up to plead for an immediate visit from the Mahatma. Once more giving his promise to go to the indigo fields in the near future, Mohandas climbed into the train. To his amazement the man followed him to the Ashram. Hardly had Gandhi greeted Kasturbai, his cousin, and his sons when he turned to see the peasant standing near the bungalow. Twirling his headgear between gnarled hands, he repeated his plea. This time Mohandas gave him a definite date for a visit.

As 1917 began, Gandhi opened his campaign for abolishing the indenture system. At a big meeting in Bombay he persuaded the leaders to announce that unless the government acted in the matter by July 31st, a strong movement of protest would be started. *Satyagraha,* the nonviolent method of disobedience, was not threatened. But everyone, including British officials, understood that it would be used.

Great excitement followed the start of the campaign. From the first, women took part in it. A group of distinguished titled and wealthy women went to New Delhi to interview the viceroy. This made an enormous impression on all English-speaking Indians. Newspaper articles vigorously attacked the evils of sending laborers out of the country on contracts. Organizations of many kinds sent resolutions to the viceroy. Such activity followed the visits Gandhi made to city after city.

Whenever he arrived at a town, the Indian notables who came to meet him at the railway station had an agonizing time finding him. In vain they searched among the travelers leaving first-class and second-class carriages. Finally, amid the pushing, chattering crowds from third-class carriages Gandhi would appear. Looking exhausted and dripping with perspiration, he would summon a smile of greeting.

To horrified protests over his mode of travel, he would reply, "But I am just a poor man like the rest. I can only afford a third-class ticket."

Usually at that point Gandhi's friends would observe a pair of men standing near by and watching his every move. Asked who on earth they were, Mohandas would say with a chuckle, "They are my bodyguards supplied by the government, detectives who do their duty very faithfully. We must tell them just where I am going to stay."

Some time before July 31st came the news for which thousands of Indians were eagerly waiting. The government announced that it had stopped the entire system of indentured emigration. It was a major triumph for Gandhi. From then on everyone knew that a great leader had come to India.

CHAPTER IX

ONE APRIL MORNING IN 1917, IN A SMALL TOWN WITHIN sight of the glittering Himalaya Mountains a tense drama was taking place. The rising sun lighted up a huge crowd massed in front of the brick courthouse. Milling about, chattering together, shouting out threats, waving sticks and hoes, hundreds of ragged peasants faced a handful of policemen who stood on the courthouse steps. The indigo workers had come to protest the arrest of Mohandas Gandhi.

For more than a week he had been traveling from village to village in the northern section of Bihar. A number of small farm owners who were unselfishly interested in the peasants had made this possible. Joined by several lawyers and a professor from a near-by school, the group had guided him, sometimes by car and sometimes on elephant back, through the plain framed by mighty mountains. Several independent farmers went with them as guides and interpreters.

In a first interview with Gandhi the local farmers said, "We have to tell you we are afraid of the big landowners. They beat and abuse us if we complain about raising indigo for them. The government always sides with the planters whatever they do. All the same we shall help all we can."

Fear! That was the atmosphere in which the majority of people lived in Bihar. Each time Gandhi walked down the single dusty street of a village he breathed it like a smell. At sight of strangers, children sprang up out of the dirt and ran to hide; women closed doors and shutters; men coming from the fields stopped in their tracks to stare in terror of they knew not what.

Nevertheless, this fog of fright blew away almost at once. None of the peasants had heard of Mahatma Gandhi. Since they could not read, they never saw a newspaper, and their tiny villages of thatched mud huts were isolated from the rest of the world. What they realized at a close glance was that a friend had come to help them. As soon as they looked into Gandhi's eyes and heard him say, "Don't be afraid," they trusted him. Strained faces brightened with the joyous astonishment of people coming out of a black dungeon into the sunlight. Like a ray of such light, news that a powerful friend was listening to what the farm workers had to say spread swiftly through the region.

Those who ruled in Bihar were equally well informed. According to his principles of fair play, Gandhi went to see both the British commissioner and the secretary of the Planters Association. He told first one and then the other that he meant to find out how much of their rented land farmers were forced to cultivate in indigo for the benefit of the landowners. Courteously he asked each man to explain the justice of demanding this work without pay. The two interviews ended in the same way. Gandhi was angrily told that he was an outsider without authority and must leave the district at once.

Frankly he warned his group of helpers. "This investigation of the unjust system carried on by Bihar planters may land us all in prison."

"This is a new idea," the men replied gravely, "but we shall not desert you."

Some days later the local magistrate, urged on by the planters, sent Gandhi an official order to leave Bihar by the next train. He sent back word that he could not and would not give up the inquiry he had been asked by the peasants to make. That very day he received a summons to appear at the courthouse for trial next morning.

All night Gandhi sat writing messages. To the viceroy he sent a telegram reporting his arrest and its cause. He wrote letters to the Ashram and to such leaders as he knew best. Early next morning he set out with several of his party for his trial.

The instant he stepped into the road, he found himself heading a procession. Men, women, and children were there as if conjured up by magic from wheat patches and

mango groves. Shouting his name, the ragged mob escorted him to the courthouse and there joined the hundreds who had come from miles around and had been waiting since the evening before.

In astonishment Gandhi asked one of his helpers, "What has become of their fear?"

Now it was the policemen who were afraid. They well knew that if the mob chose to storm the courthouse they could not be kept back. Gandhi glanced at a policeman's hand nervously fingering the pistol at his belt. "I'll help you calm these people," he said. "Let me speak to them."

From the top of the steps he called out to the crowd and they stood still to listen. "Friends," he said slowly and clearly, "you must show your faith in me and in our work by being patient and quiet. The policemen are only doing their duty. The magistrate had a perfect right to arrest me. I disobeyed his ruling that I leave Bihar. If I am sent to prison, you must accept my sentence as just. We must work together peacefully. Any violent act will hurt our good cause."

Nodding at the policeman who stared at him in astonished gratitude, Gandhi went into the building. In the courtroom were many officials and a number of planters. As the trial began, a nervous government lawyer rose to ask the magistrate to postpone the case. But Gandhi protested. He pleaded guilty and read a statement explaining why he had disobeyed the order to leave the district.

"As a law-abiding citizen I should rather have obeyed. But so great was my sense of duty to the peasants who have asked me to inquire peaceably into their troubles that I could not help choosing this course. I preferred to let the government take the responsibility of removing me from the midst of these helpless people. So proceed, gentlemen."

The officials had never faced anything like this before. The calm, friendly man in the prisoner's dock had suddenly become the judge and made his accusers feel guilty. The case was postponed. Sentence was never passed. In a few days Gandhi received two remarkable letters. The first was from the magistrate, who reported that the lieutenant governor of Bihar had ordered the case withdrawn. The second letter came from the tax collector. He said Gandhi was free to gather all the facts about the demands imposed by the planters on the peasants. Moreover, he promised that officials would help him do so.

Reporters from newspapers in near-by towns rushed to the house where Gandhi was staying. After interviewing him, they hurried away to publish the amazing story of his victory. It was wired to English and Indian journals all over the country. Gandhi had given India its first lesson in civil disobedience.

To the peasants he had given courage and hope. Not for nothing had they seen operating a force more powerful than the government. When Gandhi started his inquiry into their working conditions, they came from every corner of the indigo district to tell him their pitiful stories. Not even the presence of government secret service men at the interviews disturbed them. Each account proved that no Bihar farmer could make even a bare living if he had to raise indigo without pay.

Busy as he was taking down evidence and teaching his

helpers to accept only proved facts, Gandhi started reforms
in six villages. Adults were taught sanitation and how to use
simple home remedies. Neglected children were gathered
into primary classes held in rude shelters.

For this work Mohandas sent to the Ashram for Kasturbai and his son Manilal. He also sent to newspapers a public
appeal for volunteers. It brought to Bihar half a dozen
trained and exceptional people eager to carry out his ideas.
Among them was Mahadev Desai, a university man who
was a scholar, teacher, and writer.

When he and his wife arrived at the town where Gandhi
had his headquarters, they stared about in amazement.
With money given by a special friend, the group had rented
a house and set up tents in the open space around it. Almost a hundred peasants were seated on the ground waiting
to be interviewed. In the house at half a dozen low tables
men were writing busily, as indigo workers seated on the
floor before them told their stories. Gandhi was walking
about, listening, correcting statements, seeing that everyone, including the secret-service men, had water to drink.

Warmly welcoming the newcomers, Mohandas took
them to a quiet corner and told them his plans. Later he
escorted them to one of the forlorn and dirty villages near
by. The volunteers saw with what adoration Gandhi was
greeted and how careful he was not to show his impatience
of such homage. What he wanted was to get latrines dug
and schoolrooms opened.

Before a week was over, Mahadev Desai came to the
leader and said, "Gandhiji, my wife and I wish to devote
our lives to your work. Will you take us into your Ashram?"

Gandhi was delighted to have such a pair join his colony. He saw that no one was happier than Desai over the action of Bihar's lieutenant governor. He had appointed a committee to study the evidence collected from the indigo workers and present an opinion on it. When the report was made, the fair-minded official accepted it promptly. The planters were then obliged to refund payments to the peasants for their labor in cultivating indigo, and the unjust system of unpaid work was ended for good and all.

Gandhi said to his rejoicing helpers, "It is you who have brought this happy result to pass. Because owners of small farms and people of education have joined with the peasants to right a great wrong, the stain of indigo has been washed away!"

Mohandas was delighted on their return to the Ashram to see the warm welcome given Kasturbai. Women and children rushed to embrace her, crying, "It is good to see you, Ba!" Ba is the intimate word for mother in India and everyone felt Kasturbai's motherliness. Yet despite this joy over the returned travelers a cloud hung over the colony. Cholera had broken out in a near-by village and many of the mothers and fathers begged Gandhi to find a more healthful site for the Ashram.

This he proceeded to do. With a friend from Ahmedabad he searched the district and found a good site on the beautiful Sabarmati River just across from the town. True, in the rough field the prospectors found a number of serpents. But Mohandas said, "Somehow, I think they will not trouble us."

He had found awaiting him two important calls for help.

One was from a group of peasants in a town not far from Bombay. They wanted Gandhi to persuade the government to cancel their taxes until rain came to end the long drought afflicting the region. The earth was baked and dry. No crops would grow and the farmers were starving and penniless. The other request was from the mill workers in Ahmedabad. They had asked for higher wages and, because the mill owners would not even discuss the matter, they had decided to go on strike. But they needed Gandhi's advice.

This request he answered first. He could meet the strikers and still supervise the moving of the Ashram. Tents were set up on the new site along the Sabarmati River until huts could be built. There were now some forty people in the group and all set to work with a will.

In Ahmedabad Gandhi first talked to labor leaders and then interviewed the owners of the textile mills. A number of them were his friends and supporters of the colony. By this time most of the contributors to its support had accepted the fact that Untouchables had to belong to the Ashram. When Mohandas approached them on the matter of increased wages, however, they refused to discuss the matter.

Calling the labor leaders together, Gandhi said, "I think your cause is just. If you will accept four conditions, I will support your strike."

He demanded nonviolence during the struggle, no interference with those who would not join the strike, self-support at odd jobs instead of depending on charity during the strike, and firmness of purpose no matter how long the strike might last.

Without hesitation the leaders accepted the conditions. Then at a general meeting the strikers accepted them. Almost every day the citizens of Ahmedabad were treated to a parade of strikers proudly carrying banners which read, "Keep the pledge." Thousands of them gathered each afternoon at the new Ashram. Seated on the grass near the river, they listened to Gandhi's talks on the evils of violence and hate. "These wrong deeds and feelings," said he, "hold back progress. We must obey only the law of love."

Two weeks passed. By this time a number of strikers were growing impatient and discouraged. Their discontent brought on quarrels with strikebreakers. It was when many of them began to drift back to work that Gandhi met the situation head on. Calling together a great meeting of the men, he announced his decision on a course of action. Because he had advised the strike and had stood back of it, he had to take upon himself its failure. "I am to blame for your broken pledge," said he, "and I shall do penance for it. I shall go on a fast until the strike is settled."

For a long moment the crowd was shocked into silence. Then one of the leaders sprang up. "No! No!" he shouted, and tears began to stream down his cheeks. "You must not take the blame. It is for us to fast for wrongdoing, not you."

Groans were heard from the crowd. Shouts of "Forgive us!" and "We will take the pledge again!" filled the air. But Gandhi gently repeated his vow and the repentant workers walked soberly from the meeting.

Next day one of the mill owners who was still a warm friend of Gandhi's drove out in his car to the Ashram. He found Mohandas, with trowel in hand, helping to lay the foundation for the new weaving shed. Weaving was to be one of the main sources of income for the colony.

"Gandhiji!" called the visitor. "Are you really able to do this work? My wife and I have been very anxious about your undertaking a fast."

Dropping his trowel and folding his hands in the Indian greeting, Gandhi came forward, smiling. "Come to my tent and talk to me, my friend," said he. "I am in excellent health, as you see."

As soon as he had seated himself on Gandhi's low couch, the mill owner announced that now a compromise with the strikers was on the way. At Gandhi's expression of surprise, he burst out laughing and reported a remark made by an American manufacturer who had been visiting Ahmedabad. The American had watched the parades of strikers and heard the general lamentation over the Mahatma's fast. "Indians are amazing," he said. "I cannot imagine that in our country either strikers or employers would give a fig who fasted or why. We don't reverence leaders."

Gandhi's fast lasted just three days. The strike was settled on fair terms for the workers, and the mill owners celebrated by giving them a big party.

As soon as this happy event took place, Mohandas set off to meet the group of starving peasants who had asked for help. In their village he found a bitter struggle going on. District officials had absolutely refused to delay collecting taxes. They were confiscating cattle and any odd stores of grain as substitute for cash payment. No persuasion of Gandhi's softened their hearts.

His arrival in the village, however, had made a stir in the

big city of Bombay. Merchants, lawyers, and teachers came forward with offers of money to finance a campaign of protest. Reporters from English and Indian newspapers published daily accounts of the situation. All this hullabaloo displeased Mohandas. He wanted to keep the issue clear and the battle peaceful.

"None of these people understand the principle of *sat-yagraha*," he lamented to Mahadev Desai. "Too much hatred of the British government fills their hearts."

Nevertheless, the case was won for the peasants. Rich farmers were persuaded to fight for their cause. They announced that they would not pay a cent of taxes unless the peasants were relieved of all obligation to pay until the drought was over and crops were good again. This threat forced the government to yield. Confiscated cattle were restored to the owners and peace was made.

Not only did this victory impress all the educated people in India; the fact that it was won by cooperative effort excited them. Rich and poor, powerful and helpless had united in a single effort. As for British administrators, they learned from this affair that Gandhi was a leader to be reckoned with. To get cooperation from their subjects in a project, they had first to win over the small, quiet man called the Mahatma.

The important project facing the viceroy at the moment was to secure Indian help in the war. Although the United States had joined the Allies against Germany, no American troops had yet reached the battle front. In the spring of 1917, Germany had inflicted crushing defeats on both British and French troops in France. Turkey had held out against the English attack at Gallipoli. Russia's war effort had collapsed and the revolutionists were threatening its government. It was a black hour.

For two years Indian factories had turned out quantities of munitions. However, her vast population had taken no part in the world struggle. Now, faced with the need of fresh troops, the English looked wistfully toward their Indian subjects. It was with the idea of getting Indian volunteers that the viceroy summoned leaders to New Delhi, and Gandhi was among those invited.

During his first interview with the viceroy, Gandhi had had a favorable impression of the man. In spite of Gokhale's disillusionment, Mohandas held fast to his faith in British honor. For this reason he joined the group meeting at the capital. There he was convinced, just as he had been in the Boer War and the Zulu rebellion, that it was the duty of his fellow countrymen to fight in England's battle.

But could he persuade them? Certainly the Mohammedans created a stumbling block. For Turkey, the chief Mohammedan country, was one of England's enemies. Indeed, because of their publicly expressed sympathy with Turkey some of India's most vigorous Mohammedan patriots had been imprisoned by the government. If he supported this recruiting measure, might not Gandhi alienate those Mohammedan friends whom he so passionately longed to unite with the Hindus in every effort for progress?

Yet he had to speak the truth as he saw it. Rising to face the viceroy and his fellow Indians from the congress, Gandhi turned to the former with a smile. "May I speak in

Hindustani?" And when the Englishman nodded, he said solemnly, "With a full sense of responsibility I beg to support the resolution to recruit volunteers."

Only one sentence! Yet because at an official conference it was not spoken in English but in Hindustani, the sentence made a deep impression. For the first time a man had dared to shun the language of the conquerors.

Before Gandhi started recruiting volunteers for the British army, he wrote the viceroy a long statement. Without trying to make a bargain in return for his freely offered service, he said he did expect that after the war ended England would begin to organize home rule for India. He assured the viceroy that not only educated citizens but also simple farmers and peasants now wanted political freedom. Religious differences were being submerged in patriotic fervor. The Moslem League had made an alliance with the Indian Congress to demand self-government. England, concluded Gandhi, could count on a peaceful and happy people only if she granted them self-rule. The letter was published in all important newspapers.

His recruiting efforts nearly ruined Gandhi's health. He often walked twenty miles a day from village to village to make speeches and interview young men. Suddenly his strength gave out and he became extremely ill. For a time he thought he might die and his family and friends had the same fear.

Kasturbai never left his side. One morning she stood with the doctor beside her husband's bed. Both were anxious and bewildered. Kasturbai laid a finger on her husband's thin arm and said, "The doctor wants you to drink milk.

I know you have vowed never to drink cow's milk, but you took no vow not to touch the milk of goats. Why not try that if you wish to get well? Isn't your work worth this sacrifice?"

Feebly Mohandas smiled up at the two worried faces. "Poor souls, you have a crank to nurse! Very well, although it goes against my conscience to break my vow, I'll drink goat's milk."

Very slowly he gained strength. One day he sat propped up on his bed reading the newspapers. It was plain in this early summer of 1918 that the Allies were going to win the war. Turning from reports of their gains on the battlefield, he noticed an announcement of a new bill just presented to the Indian government. It was a measure to prevent possible uprisings. The government was to be given power to imprison without trial and to try in secret without jury any person suspected of disloyal activity.

Gandhi fell back as if he had received a blow. At that moment Mahadev Desai, who was now acting as Gandhi's secretary, entered the room with a pile of letters. Mohandas pointed out the item in the journal and gasped out, "Look! Just look at this!"

Desai's face grew pale as he read. "I can't believe it!" he exclaimed. "It's terrorism! Do Englishmen mean to over-throw in India all the principles they believe in? Think how they fought and worked for centuries in their own country to defend the rights of the individual!"

Gandhi's dark eyes were smoldering. "All India must protest this bill. No people with a shred of self-respect could submit to such an attack on their liberties."

That very day several of the leaders from Ahmedabad came out for consultation. They helped Gandhi in the next weeks to organize a protest. First of all, a league was formed to spread the doctrine of *satyagraha*. From his bed Gandhi wrote articles for Indian papers, to explain how nonviolent opposition to tyranny could be made in a loving spirit of self-sacrifice. He cited the new bill as an act of tyranny. As soon as possible, he dragged himself up to make speeches in several cities. To the viceroy he addressed private letters and public appeals begging him to take a stand against the bill.

In the midst of these activities came news that Germany had surrendered. The terrible war was over. In this land as in every land flags were flying, bells were ringing, and people rejoiced together.

Yet there was no peace in India. As 1918 ended and 1919 began, storm clouds gathered ever more thickly. From the battle front thousands of soldiers, deeply affected by contact with Westerners, were coming back to all parts of the country. As workers in munition factories were laid off, cities filled with the unemployed.

In the political field the prospect was gloomy. Loyal support in the "war for democracy" had won nothing for the Indians. No move was made toward giving the people a constitution. A few unimportant measures were introduced to allow the minority a little more responsibility. But at the same time the government passed the bill granting itself illegal powers of arrest and punishment of suspected persons.

Although the quiet routine of the Sabarmati Ashram was unbroken, although the bell for morning prayers rang at four in the morning and Gandhi took his brisk walk before breakfast, kept an eye on all activities, and held his prayer meeting at sunset, everyone was aware of intense undercurrents. Day by day men of importance from many parts of India drove from the Ahmedabad station to Gandhi's thatched cottage. Conferences on his veranda were held each day. Enormous heaps of letters came and went.

"Now we must act," Gandhi kept saying. "Since all our protests have been in vain, we must work out a means of refusing to accept this new tyranny."

On February 28th he sent to the press a pledge for all brave men to sign. They were to promise to be ready to undertake nonviolent disobedience. With the pledge was printed a manifesto announcing that a general *satyagraha*

would soon be called. Then with Mahadev Desai he started
on a round of speeches at various cities.

When they reached Allahabad, a small city not far from
Benares, a message was waiting for Gandhi. He read it with
surprise. It was from Motilal Nehru, the wealthy Brahmin
lawyer whom he had met at the Indian Congress almost
three years before. In spite of the fact that this conservative man was not in sympathy with *satyagraha*, he had invited Gandhi to his house.

A handsome motor car was sent to bring Mohandas to
that interview. As he got out, he looked about curiously.
The driveway, curving at one side of the superb garden, was
lined with hibiscus plants set between palm and pome-
granate trees. On the enormous space fronting the mansion
was a tennis court and a summerhouse covered with flower-
ing vines. Behind it the visitor caught a glimpse of a fruit
orchard stretching back to the walled compound facing the
servants' quarters.

Gandhi was warmly greeted by his host and taken into a
study lined with books and furnished in Western style.
Without wasting an instant, the lawyer began to talk with
vigorous frankness, and Gandhi found himself even more
strongly drawn to him than he had been at their first meeting. Here, he thought, is a person of force and sterling character. He may not be ready yet, but some day he will help
guide us through our battle for freedom.

"It is my son Jawaharlal of whom I wish to speak," said
Nehru. "He has been deeply moved by your discussion of
satyagraha. Jawaharlal has been so disgusted with the do-
nothing policy of congress and of most businessmen that

he wants to join your party of action. But neither he nor I realized at first that you really want people to court arrest and imprisonment. I see no sense, Gandhiji, in clever, much-needed men going to jail. My son and I have argued by the hour. I am opposed to his embarking on such a course."

"That I understand," replied Gandhi gently. He smiled at the man in his well-tailored English clothes. "The sacrifice is heavy. No one should undertake *satyagraha* who is not fully ready for the perils involved. Nevertheless, this is the most effective protest against a tyrannical government that any people can make."

Over the whole household that evening Mohandas shed his affectionate interest. Motilal's sensitive wife, his handsome elder daughter, and Jawaharlal's beautiful young bride, all three wearing on their foreheads the small red circle with which high-caste Brahmin women adorn themselves, Jawaharlal and his father—this tightly knit family seemed to the visitor an almost perfect group of its kind. He could find it in his heart to wish that nothing might threaten its security and joy.

At dinner they sat on cushions on the veranda enclosed in colonnades. A fine tablecloth was spread upon the tiled floor and servants swiftly served curries, wheat cakes, rice, pepper water, sweets, and fruits. It was a merry party.

"Please forgive me," Gandhi said, "for refusing so many of these exquisite dishes. I am a most unsatisfactory guest."

Motilal gave a hearty boom of laughter. "Ah, tonight we are serving in the Indian style in your honor. There is a dining room on the other side of the hall with a banquet table and on it we serve roast beef, potatoes, and puddings in the English fashion."

Before he left, Gandhi had a long talk with the youthful Jawaharlal. He strongly advised him to bide his time and not plunge into action at once. "You can safely leave things to India's unfolding destiny. Your father is too noble a man and too great a patriot to stand aside or to ask you to do so when the need for personal sacrifice becomes clear."

Gandhi's next sojourn was at Madras on the southeast coast. He had addressed meetings there before and was welcomed by an enthusiastic audience. His host was a lawyer deeply interested in political problems. He and several other leaders tried to thrash out with Mohandas a plan of action. Something more than merely holding public meetings had to be done. But what?

One early morning Mohandas came into the garden where the group was already gathered. The fragrance of jasmine flowers, the shine of marigolds, the fresh sunlit air gave the scene a joyousness which was reflected on Gandhi's face.

"My friends," he cried, "I have been given an inspiration in a dream. Let us announce to all the millions of our people that they should set aside a day of prayer and mourning as a public protest against this insulting new law. Let no work be done except what is essential for the public good. All can join in such a peaceful expression of reproach."

"A day of prayer, a *hartal!*" exclaimed the lawyer excitedly. "A *hartal* in which rich and poor, people of all religions can unite. That is it! We must choose a day at once and announce it in the press."

Since there was need of haste, April 6th, 1919, was chosen. "Of course," said Gandhi, "we have little time to organize the demonstration. All we can do is to spread word of it to all the provinces. We could hardly expect a complete response throughout the country."

By April 4th Gandhi reached Bombay. He was in time to start the ceremonies there with an enormous parade. But Bombay was only one small part of the extraordinary spectacle that met the eyes of the British on April 6th. For then the clock stopped in India. Not a wheel turned in a factory. Every shop was closed. No farmer went out with his plow. In cities, towns, and tiny villages from the Himalayas to the tip of the peninsula, the *hartal* was celebrated. Mohammedans, Hindus, Parsis, Buddhists, people of every faith, joined together in fasting, prayer, and peaceful processions. The stricken face of India was turned to its rulers in eloquent appeal.

Too eloquent! Such unity of protest frightened the governors of almost four hundred million people. Fear drove the British to acts which changed the whole temper of the country and stamped a new pattern on the life of Mohandas Gandhi.

CHAPTER X

IT WAS AT DELHI THAT THE BRITISH STRUCK FIRST. THE very moment he reached Bombay, Gandhi received a long telegram from a religious leader in Delhi. British police had tried to stop a peaceful parade and then opened fire on the crowd, killing a number and injuring many. "Come quickly," read the message.

Gandhi, however, had first to fulfill his obligations to the *hartal* in Bombay. With his old acquaintance, Mrs. Sarajini Naidu, he addressed a large audience of Hindus and Mohammedans gathered in a Mohammedan mosque. This was a unique event in the history of India. Never before had anyone but a Mohammedan lifted his voice inside a mosque.

Hardly had he returned from a day of impressive ceremonies in which the entire Indian population took part, when more telegrams arrived. They were sent from two cities in the northern district called the Punjab. In Lahore, the capital, and in Amritsar fierce clashes had occurred between police and people. "Come to us," wired the anxious leaders. "We know not what to do." Mahadev Desai hurriedly telegraphed back that Gandhi would go to the Punjab from Delhi.

These passionate appeals from three cities were made in vain. On the way to Delhi Gandhi was taken from the train by police and was sent back to Bombay under guard. "Your presence," they explained, "will only excite the crowds still more. There is rioting in the Punjab."

"But they don't know me there," answered Gandhi with a skeptical smile.

At Bombay he was freed at once. He reached a friend's house to learn that an enormous crowd had gathered not far from the fort below the city. News of his arrest had excited the entire population. "Only you can prevent a riot, Gandhiji," said the friend. "I will take you to the spot in my car."

As the car arrived at the edge of the crowd, Gandhi was recognized at once and greeted with frenzied joy. Cheering and shouting, the people formed a procession of escort and ran before, behind, and beside the slowly moving automobile. Suddenly a troop of mounted police barred the way. "Charge!" cried the officer in command. Gandhi saw the horsemen plunge forward with lowered lances. Screams from trampled men, women, and children filled his ears. Madly the crowd and its pursuers rushed past his car and in another moment the street was empty.

Trembling with the shock of this scene, Gandhi gasped to his friend, "Take me at once to the commissioner's office."

They found the official building swarming with armed

guards. The commissioner, flushed with anger and excitement, was in no mood to receive Gandhi's courteous protest against the bloodthirsty cavalry charge.

"We had to use stern measures in order to quell the mob," he shouted. "People do not understand your idea of peaceful disobedience of law. Do you know what is happening in Ahmedabad and the Punjab? Indians have gone mad everywhere and these disturbances are your responsibility."

Gandhi heard this statement with sinking heart. Violence! This was contrary to the very essence of *satyagraha*. The brutal methods of police excused no one for breaking the pledge to protest peaceably.

Officials in Bombay were quite willing to let Gandhi go to Ahmedabad. "See for yourself the outrages your disciples have committed!" they said. Then they sent word for a police guard to meet him at the Ahmedabad station and take him to the district commissioner.

On the way through the town, Mohandas looked around in despair. Troops were scattered about the deserted streets. No gay groups of people were shopping and chattering in the bazaars. Only the monkeys swinging from tall peepul trees gave the place an air of life. Fear and distrust seemed to brood over Ahmedabad.

Gandhi was received gravely by his old acquaintance, the commissioner, and was told what had happened. The mill hands had gone on strike, damaged property, and killed a police sergeant. Rails had been torn up on railroad tracks and a government official had been murdered. In a near-by town similar rioting had occurred.

"All this, Mr. Gandhi," concluded the official, "was mainly in defiance of the government's precaution in arresting you. For the same reason there were fresh outbreaks in the Punjab. Is this your widely advertised peaceful protest?"

Every word pierced Gandhi's heart like a dagger. He had failed. His people were not ready for *satyagraha*. They could not act lovingly. The profound regret he uttered softened the commissioner's attitude. He readily gave Mohandas permission to hold a meeting of the mill workers at the Ashram.

To that gathering and to another in the neighboring town Gandhi spoke as a sorrowful father to erring sons. He announced the end of civil disobedience. "I have made a Himalayan miscalculation," said he. "Indians do not understand how to make a peaceful protest. A man must respect law and order before he can properly refuse to obey an unjust law. Self-control, self-sacrifice, regard for those who oppose you—such are the requirements for *satyagraha*. My penance for starting this untimely program of protest is a three-day fast."

All the care which Kasturbai and the other residents of the Ashram lavished upon the leader failed to lift his spirits. The many young men who had joined the colony, like the young men in every city and province, were furious to have *satyagraha* stopped. English reporters were making merry over Gandhi's phrase, "Himalayan miscalculation." But neither ridicule nor criticism moved him. He sent to the press one article after another condemning the riots. He urged strikers to go back to work and the members of the

satyagraha league to strive to restore order. By every means
—speeches, personal interviews, and the publication of leaflets—he taught the true way of nonviolent resistance.

This was no easy task. Most people thought blame
should rest on the police who broke up peaceful meetings.
Moreover, there was a widespread suspicion that the government was terrorizing the Punjab. No one was allowed
either to enter or leave that district. Reporters could get no
official facts from General Dyer, a British army commander
who now ruled the province. Nevertheless, as if borne by
the wind, ugly rumors of the persecution of Punjabi citizens
drifted about the entire country.

One warm May afternoon Gandhi was in Bombay. Coming back from seeing a local leader who lived at the edge of
the city, he heard the slow creaking of cart wheels behind
him and turned around. The look of extreme exhaustion
on the face of the driver, the staggering weariness of the
two bullocks, startled him and he stepped into the road. At
once the beasts stopped in their tracks and the driver, with
terror in his eyes, cried in a weak voice, "What do you
want?"

"To help you, my friend," replied Gandhi gently. "You
look as if you were at the end of your strength. Have you
a place to stay? How far have you come?"

Wild bloodshot eyes looked into Gandhi's face. In a
whisper the man said, "I escaped. They did not see me
cross the border in the dark, those murderers!"

In consternation Gandhi said with a flash of intuition,
"You come from the Punjab!"

Nodding, the man bent lower over the cart rail. "Oh,

you don't know! What awfulness . . . the massacre . . . hundreds dead. My poor wife, my two sons, they were in that place. I know not where they are buried." He broke into shuddering sobs.

Even after Gandhi had guided the refugee to the house of a friend in the Untouchable quarter of Bombay, he could obtain no coherent account of the horrors from which the man had fled. But the very next day he received a long letter from Mr. Andrews, who had been allowed to enter the isolated district. Guardedly Andrews described the severe martial law established in cities and villages of the Punjab and hinted at an attack by soldiers on a peaceful group of citizens.

Andrews begged his friend to come to the Punjab. Already Gandhi had asked permission to do so from the viceroy and had been refused. Now he again sought permission and once more it was denied. But from refugees drifting day by day into Bombay not only Gandhi but also the newspapermen were getting the grim facts.

Trouble had started in Amritsar on April 6th, 1919, the day of the *hartal*. When police broke up the processions, the crowd resisted. Then clubs were used by police and many arrests were made. Immediately General Dyer brought troops into the city and took command of the Punjab. He declared martial law and forbade gatherings of any kind.

Nevertheless, on April 13th a large group of people gathered in Amritsar to make a petition of protest. The meeting was held in a public garden. The place, surrounded by a wall and buildings, had but one exit. Hearing of the forbidden meeting, Dyer marched troops armed with machine guns to the garden. The soldiers fired sixteen hundred rounds into the unarmed mass of people. At the first shot the exit was jammed and there was no escape for the crowd. Nearly four hundred people were killed and twelve hundred were wounded. Leaving the wounded and dying on the ground, the troops marched away.

From then on Dyer tried by every means to break the spirit of Amritsar citizens. They had to salute every passing officer with bended knees. Failure to do so or to obey the curfew ordinance was punished by public floggings. In revenge for a mob attack on an English nurse during the excitement of April 6th, anyone having to enter the street where she lived was obliged to crawl on all fours. A pall of terror enveloped the city. And all this went on unknown to most of India and to England and the world for four dreadful months.

When Indian papers published the first full report, the whole country was in turmoil. Gandhi, to whom members of the congress and heads of various societies turned for advice, insisted that only by fasting and prayer could people reach the right mood for dealing with the outrage. He himself, shaken to the depths, spent hours alone in thought. Before him arose the ugly sequence of British acts in the past twelve months. Moreover, England's indifference to the suffering she inflicted on her Mohammedan subjects by delays in signing the peace treaty with Turkey shocked him as much as it angered them.

Mahadev Desai was the first to learn the direction of Gandhi's intense thinking. One night as the two men, wrapped in cloaks, sat on the veranda at the Ashram, Mohandas opened his heart.

"The events of this year," he said slowly, "have changed my feeling as to what is essential work now for India. Poverty and famine, ignorance, the spread of plagues, the long idleness in villages during the winter—these woes cry out for healing. But I see at last that they will not be healed until we ourselves have real power in the government. Political freedom is our one hope."

Desai turned to him in great excitement. Here, indeed, was a decisive shift of purpose. "Go on, Gandhiji! Tell me how we shall win freedom against the powerful British. They are determined to keep us by force as an absolutely dependent colony."

"We shall win it by campaigns of education," said Mohandas promptly, "carried on until our millions are ready for *satyagraha*; by unceasing pressure from a forceful congress; by the might of nonviolent resistance. I tell you, my dear friend, no government can hold out against the spirit of brave sacrifice on the part of a whole people, not even the most tyrannical conquerors. And the British are not that. Their constitution is still my admiration."

He cited the split in English opinion when General Dyer's record became known. Conservatives and imperialists raised a large sum of money as a reward for Dyer's swift suppression of rebellion. But the liberals forced Parliament to appoint a committee of inquiry into the Punjab affair. Unfortunately they were unable to prevent the committee from consisting entirely of English members. Indians, therefore, proceeded to boycott it.

For months Gandhi's request that he be allowed to make his own investigation was refused. Finally in October the viceroy sent him a permit to enter the Punjab. At Lahore, the district capital, Gandhi was met at the station by so many thousands of cheering people that it looked as if the entire population had turned out. The faces turned up to the little dark man on the car steps were filled with reverence. It was as if they welcomed the spirit of truth in human form.

Hardly had Mohandas settled his few belongings in the house of a friend, when crowds began to invade his host's garden. Everyone wanted to tell his own story of what he had gone through during Dyer's military occupation. In no time at all Gandhi was conducting his own private inquiry into the Punjab atrocities.

It was far more extensive than that of the boycotted government investigation and as he could not undertake the giant task alone, the congress appointed a committee to help him. Motilal Nehru was in charge of organizing the inquiry both in Amritsar and Lahore. His son Jawaharlal also came to help. So it was that the young aristocrat and the Mahatma grew to know one another.

They were an odd combination. Young Nehru, trained in English schools, had only one vital connection with religion. He reverenced his pious mother. Gandhi's religious approach to every kind of problem was hard for him to follow. Yet Jawaharlal realized that the masses of people were drawn to the leader just because his thought, his deeds, and his way of living expressed the spiritual quality they adored. Nehru's approval was aroused by the scientific accuracy with which Gandhi ferreted out the exact truth in the tales told by Dyer's victims.

One of the many duties which called Gandhi away from supervising the investigation in the Punjab was the necessity of attending a conference of Mohammedans. They wanted Gandhi to plan a way to force England to make a favorable treaty with her defeated enemy, Turkey. For Turkey was the land of the Caliph, keeper of the Mohammedan faith, and as important to Mohammedans the world over as Rome is to Catholics. England's proposed treaty was purely political and ignored the religious passion which was ready to resent any lack of respect for their leader.

The Mohammedan committee decided, on Gandhi's advice, to start a boycott of foreign cloth. Gandhi also suggested a program of noncooperation with the British. Finding that he meant them to give up their British titles and posts of honor, these wealthy noblemen made a very half-hearted response.

Then with a bit of steel behind his gentleness Gandhi said, "If I am leader, you must set an example of self-sacrifice. The moment you are dissatisfied with me, I'll gladly resign."

Back to the Punjab he went to help prepare the report to the congress on the interviews with seventeen hundred citizens. It was near the end of 1919 when the annual meeting of the congress opened at Amritsar. As soon as the members arrived, they visited the garden where the massacre took place as if it were a holy shrine. The final report of atrocities and humiliations suffered by Indians in the Punjab stirred them to the depths. Even the most conservative now wanted effective action toward getting a national government. No one was more influential in this direction than a new leader, Mr. C. R. Das.

Before the session started, Motilal Nehru took Gandhi aside. "This time, Gandhiji, you cannot be merely a spectator. I see everyone rushing up to consult you. You must advise us as to the measures we should take."

Motilal Nehru was president of the congress that December. Observing him closely, Mohandas saw that he was

not the man of two years ago who had tried to keep his son safely sheltered. So deeply was he pained by the sufferings of his countrymen in the Punjab that his old conservative pattern of moderate policy was destroyed. His only concern now was to win political freedom.

The session promised to be exciting. Vigorous new members were on hand. One of the radical Mohammedans, a bitter enemy of England, had just been released from prison and was given a warm welcome. Quite a different person was another man of the same faith, M. A. Jinnah. He was wealthy, fashionably dressed in the English style, and the very pattern of good form. Jinnah was a strong advocate of unity between Mohammedans and Hindus. He was one of the many who were eager for Gandhi's advice on various measures.

Forced by popular demand to take part in the session, Gandhi started out by advocating the adoption of a resolution to support England's first move to give India a constitution. It was a poor, weak instrument which did not advance self-government very far. But Gandhi thought the British should be encouraged. Bitter opposition to this proposal came from the many foes of Great Britain.

After a long confused discussion of the subject, there was an intermission. Gandhi walked out of the hall with Motilal Nehru, who had been one of his supporters.

"You know, Motilalji," said he, "the congress can accomplish nothing by the hit-or-miss methods used. The meeting hall is always swarming with visitors and spectators. Votes cannot be counted accurately. None but members should attend important sessions. Nor should any nonmember be allowed to speak. What's more, each district should have fair representation."

Motilal Nehru's fine thoughtful face lighted up. "You are right, Gandhiji. Let us weld ourselves into a body fit for action."

Thereupon Gandhi was given the task of drafting a new constitution for the congress. With his quick legal brain he worked out in a few months' time a practical method of elections and of handling business at the sessions and by committees. From then on the congress took on new life and drive. Its guiding spirit was Mohandas Gandhi.

The year 1920 was a banner year for him. Hundreds of men young and old had joined the Congress Party and were eagerly taking up Gandhi's suggestions. Many older men had followed his example in withdrawing from British patronage. Gandhi returned to the viceroy the medal he had received for his war services. Rabindranath Tagore had asked the government to abolish the title it had bestowed upon him. Others resigned from high posts in the civil service.

Meanwhile a project Mohandas had long desired to push became a reality. For years he had been urging Indians to wear home-woven clothes. In newspaper articles, books, and speeches he declared it was absurd to send to England the yarn spun in India from cotton grown there and then import highly taxed cotton cloth woven in English mills. Because weaving had grown into quite an industry at the Ashram, a considerable number of people already wore clothes woven there. But it was hard for the weavers to get cotton yarn. Only as a favor and at a high price would mills in Ahmedabad sell yarn to Gandhi's followers.

"If we could only get spinning wheels and teach villagers to spin!" That was what Mohandas kept saying everywhere he went. "With spinning wheels we could accomplish two things at a stroke. Villagers could earn extra money in the winter and weavers could get as much yarn as they need."

Finally a woman who was a devoted follower of Gandhi answered his appeal. She actually found a number of spinning wheels stored away in the homes of some factory workers she knew. Next she hunted down several old farm women who knew how to spin. Gandhi's joy at these discoveries knew no bounds. He raised funds to cover the expense of bringing wheels and spinners to the Ashram. Somehow, an old fellow was unearthed who could card raw cotton and make slivers for spinning thread.

Then, indeed, all was set for the project so dear to Gandhi's heart. Mahadev Desai devised a small practical wheel which could be easily manufactured, and he then set up a factory at the Ashram. One by one all the colonists, men and women alike, were taught by the old spinners to spin thread. A special group learned to card cotton. As soon as humming wheels turned in every hut and the weaving shed was stacked with thread, this hand industry began to spread across India. From the Ashram, teachers with wagon loads of spinning wheels went to villages and taught the peasants how to spin.

The poor people were glad to learn a craft with which they could earn a little extra for necessities. But as time went on, they understood that something far more important was happening to them. To hear that congress members and professors, rich women and high-caste girls were also becoming skilled spinners thrilled the villagers with a sense of belonging to one people. No longer were they alone and forgotten in their village homes. Threads of cotton were binding everyone together. Slowly they grasped what the intellectuals had seen at once. The *charka*, as the spinning wheel is called in India, had become a symbol of national unity and independence.

The year 1920 was also marked by another of Gandhi's

innovations. At a special congress session he proposed a resolution to undertake nonviolent noncooperation. Many members were against the idea because they did not trust people to follow it. Others hesitated through disbelief in absolute nonviolence.

Motilal Nehru, however, was in favor of it. He said to Gandhi, "We must make it plain that noncooperation is a means to force the British to give India self-government. Add that to your resolution and I shall support it."

Gandhi was not convinced that India was ready yet to govern herself. But he listened to Nehru, to Jinnah, and to C. R. Das. Graciously, tactfully, he made concessions. Persuasively he won more and more converts to his program of action.

At the regular meeting in December, the well-organized congress passed five important measures introduced by Gandhi. Noncooperation was to include boycott of all English schools and colleges; boycott of foreign cloth; boycott of English courts of law and of the British-dominated local elections; the wearing of homespun by members of congress; and a resolution against the continuation of Untouchability.

That Hindu members spoke out against Untouchability gave dramatic proof of Gandhi's influence. The resolution astounded the whole world. For three thousand years the belief that a group of persons were untouchable had been part of India's caste system. Until Gandhi set the example by accepting these degraded people as friends and co-workers, until in books and articles he publicly attacked the practice as unholy, no one had dared dispute it.

Indeed, the whole political picture of India had changed. For a meek congress devoted to friendly relations with England, Gandhi had substituted a body of ardent workers and a definite program in which all could join. Slowly the masses were being taught to obey the resolutions of the Indian Congress instead of the decrees of the British government.

It was not long before the entire country had visible proof of resistance to English rule. Members of the congress were clad in homespun cotton, a material called *khadi*. When wealthy leaders appeared in their offices or at public meetings dressed in dhotis, shirts, and coats made of homespun, the British were startled and all the followers of Gandhi were thrilled. A little pointed white cotton beret, known everywhere as the Gandhi cap, became the most popular headgear in the land.

On a visit to the Nehru family Mohandas had a close view of the tremendous changes taking place in personal lives. He had come to talk over details of the new program with Motilal. Jawaharlal Nehru wore for the first time the Gandhi cap perched jauntily on the side of his handsome dark head.

"A great idea, Gandhiji!" said the youth gaily. "With all congress members in *khadi* uniforms, everyone knows at a glance that we're for home rule. Besides, if enough people follow our example, we'll really stop imports of British cloth."

Delightedly Gandhi turned to Motilal. "As for you, my friend, in your white cotton robe you look like a sage of olden times."

There followed a sociable hour with several guests gathered in the big drawing room. For the first time Gandhi met his host's youngest daughter, a small girl who stared shyly at the quiet man. Her dark eyes seemed to ask, "Is this really the person who has turned our home upside down?"

For the mansion was a changed place. Motilal Nehru had pledged himself utterly to the struggle for his country's freedom. Faithful to the vow of noncooperation with the English courts, he had given up most of the law practice which had brought him a large income. To support his family he had sold his valuable china and glass, his riding horses and cars. Half his army of servants had been dismissed, and the simplicity of daily meals matched his *khadi* clothes. Implicitly also he had obeyed the congressional resolution to boycott English schools.

"I understand," said Mohandas to Motilal's small daughter, "that your father has taken you out of your English school. Never mind. We hope soon to have good Indian schools for young ladies like you."

She tossed back her head. "Worse than stopping our going to school is that you won't let anybody revenge the awful murders at Amritsar."

Looking deep into her eyes, Mohandas said gently, "If you are naughty, don't you expect your family to forgive you and love you? Only a few of the English people have been wicked. We have to learn that all human beings belong to one family—God's children, every one."

Both man and child were unaware that most of the people in the room were now listening to this dialogue. As if bewitched, the little girl drew close to the figure sitting cross-legged on the low couch. "You know," said she in a dreamy tone, "I thought you would be very tall and strong and that your eyes would flash fire."

A burst of laughter followed this remark. Gandhi joined it gleefully. "I must be very disappointing," he said.

Looking around, much abashed, the child turned to her mother, who had come to lead her away, and hid her face in the folds of Mrs. Nehru's cotton sari. She did not see the look of adoring gratitude her mother bestowed on Gandhi.

That evening Jawaharlal Nehru deeply interested Gandhi by an account of his first contact with peasants. With an experienced member of the congress he had gone up to the farming region in a province north of Allahabad. They had been asked by a peasant leader to investigate the crushing demands of tax collectors.

"It was a great experience," said the young man eagerly. "When word was spread that we were holding a meeting, peasants came tramping over the fields by the thousands, even from miles away. I was surprised to find I could talk to these simple people. I told them about our plans for wearing *khadi* and about our demand for self-government which would bring relief to taxpayers. I reported that we were against Untouchability. Of course, they didn't like that. Peasants are just as prejudiced as anybody else. But they were excited over us. Nobody had ever paid attention to them before. Gandhiji, it's wicked that city people like me have lived apart in our comfortable small world. We are so few compared to the untold millions of farm and village folk."

Gandhi's face was radiant. He exclaimed softly, "You have touched the heart of India. If we can get the peasants to understand these principles, we can really offer a nation-wide noncooperation program."

From that time on he looked upon Jawaharlal Nehru as a coming leader.

Young Nehru's experience was shared by many congress members. They went to villages in every part of the country to tell the peasants of the peaceful struggle being organized. Meanwhile, Gandhi was traveling much of the time. At colleges, at conferences with Mohammedans, and to groups of every sort he discussed noncooperation. He, an admirer of the British constitution, was preaching peaceful opposition to the government for three reasons. There had been no redress for the Punjab horrors. England's prime minister, unmindful both of his own pledge and of the religious passion of seventy million Mohammedan citizens, had drafted a severe treaty with Turkey. In addition, the law permitting arrest and imprisonment of suspects was still in force.

One of Gandhi's public statements had wide circulation. He had said, "I consider the ways of this government immoral, unjust, debasing, and untruthful. Until we have wrung justice and our self-respect from the unwilling hands of the British, there can be no cooperation."

The radical young men in the congress had formed the National Volunteer Corps, wore *khadi* uniforms, drilled in public squares, and peacefully picketed shops selling foreign cloth. Everywhere leaders were speaking and writing in the most fearless fashion. The whole country was bursting with joyous energy and hope.

In May of 1921, Motilal Nehru gave his friends a last experience of lavish entertainment. The wedding of his elder daughter was celebrated in the grand style, with hundreds of guests, majestic feasts, music, and gaiety. In order to be sure of Gandhi's presence, a meeting of the Congress Working Committee was arranged at Allahabad at that time. Also a local conference was slated at which thousands of peasants and farmers were expected.

After the wedding ceremony at the Nehru mansion, during the height of the celebration, Jawaharlal drew away from a group of lovely young ladies in exquisite rainbow-hued saris. He threaded the gaily chatting groups, waved aside the servants presenting trays of ices, turned a deaf ear to elegant youths calling his name, and finally stopped at the edge of a group in a quiet corner. Sitting in the middle of it on the floor was Gandhi. Lately he had adopted the costume of the poorest peasant or Untouchable. It consisted of a brief loincloth and a pair of sandals. Around his bare body a cotton cloak was loosely draped. He and the others were laughing gaily.

"Gandhiji," cried Jawaharlal, "I have a new tale of British stupidity. Today I learned from a lawyer in Allahabad that all these meetings and commotions have terrified our rulers. They think a frightful revolt is brewing. They've even got the fort on the edge of town ready to receive English refugees."

Throwing back his head, the young man roared with laughter. Mrs. Sarajini Naidu, who was one of the group, echoed his mirth. "Imagine," she exclaimed. "Those people will never understand us. We've made no secret of anything. But they always think we're mysterious—a race of plotters!"

Gandhi smiled but shook his head. "I share this nervousness to some extent," he said slowly. "There is tension everywhere and amid a suppressed people there is always danger of violence. To me violence is against religion, contrary to the spirit. I keep on hoping England will right the wrongs she has done us before it is too late."

For an instant the group was silent. Few of the people standing there shared this hope. What they wanted was action, a dash for freedom. Yet the grave words of their leader touched them. Vividly there arose before their eyes the picture of this frail brown figure striding across India to bring all people courage for self-sacrifice. They saw him speaking to thousands, tramping to villages, writing letters on the trains, inspiring Mohammedans with the determination to work with Hindus.

Yet honesty compelled Nehru to murmur, "England will not change her policy—never until she is forced to do so."

He was right. Six months later the government swooped down upon the patriots, and India became a land of persecuted people.

CHAPTER XI

IN 1921 THE WHOLE WORLD WAS WATCHING THE INDIAN situation. England's fear of revolution in her colony was known from sea to sea. In Europe and America newspapers had begun to feature the human drama of a small middle-aged man, garbed only in a loincloth, defying the mighty British Empire and doing so by preaching passive resistance against it.

Journalists were often sent by their chiefs to interview Mohandas Gandhi. On first arrival at the Ashram they were highly entertained by its oddities. They saw Gandhi leave a conference with Motilal Nehru and members of the Congress Working Committee in order to make a mud poultice for a sick child. They heard everyone addressing the famous leader as *Bapu*, Father, and observed that his concern for others was returned in devotion.

Kasturbai set the example. At the noonday dinner of vegetables, wheat cakes, and fruit served in the general dining room, the correspondents placed on either side of Gandhi kept watching Kasturbai. She never stopped waving a big fan to keep flies and gnats at a distance from her husband. During his rest period she stood guard at his hut or placed someone else there to receive visitors. At that hour even the children were hushed. Only the hum of spinning wheels and the bang and click of looms broke the silence.

Merrily Gandhi would ask the newspapermen, "How do you like our circus?" Sometimes he even teasingly suggested that if they took their turns at drawing water from the well, he would be the more ready to answer questions.

His discussion of India's problems was always frank and friendly. Listeners not only enjoyed themselves but were deeply impressed by Gandhi's keen intellect and vast knowledge of his country. Before leaving the colony on the Sabarmati River, many of the correspondents attended the evening prayer meeting. Its strange music, Gandhi's brief talk—perhaps showing how the Sermon on the Mount was a teaching of *satyagraha*—the moment of silent meditation, all wove a spell about the Westerners. It held as darkness closed in. For then the place sparkled with the little lanterns which everyone had to carry to avoid stepping on snakes.

Spring brought a new viceroy to India. At the suggestion of Mr. C. F. Andrews, whom every viceroy consulted, Gandhi was asked to come to the palace and state his views in person. The invitation was promptly accepted.

On his return to the Ashram from the interview, Mohandas said to Mahadev Desai, "As man to man I could talk to the viceroy. But behind the sympathetic individual was always the imperial official. I could feel how he was pressed by parliament and capitalists at home not to give in. Money, world prestige, trade—so much of England is tied up in the domination of our country. The British fear the slightest lessening of power."

What was the government going to do? Few arrests were made all summer. Then suddenly came an official announcement which set all India laughing. A great honor was to be bestowed upon the country. The Prince of Wales was arriving for a visit and would meet his loyal subjects at various splendid entertainments.

Gandhi read these headlines in the paper one morning just before a conference with a group of congress leaders. He shattered their mirth over the news by an indignant outburst. "The British think we are children! Parades for the prince are to make us forget the Punjab, the Turkish treaty, and the everlasting delay in giving us a constitution!"

On his advice the Congress Working Committee declared that all parades and celebrations were to be strictly boycotted. With every care to preserve the safety of the young prince, Indian citizens were urged to shun this demonstration of imperial power. In August down at Madras on the east coast fifty thousand people gathered on the beach to hear Gandhi. Detail by detail, he explained the program which was to involve the whole country.

"This visit of the Prince of Wales," said he, "has been arranged to tighten the government's hold on the national neck. We do not suggest boycotting His Royal Highness as a person, but as an instrument of oppression. We can show the world that such noncooperation is just the reverse of Europe's doctrine of the sword. Let us act in accord with the holy prophets of old. Noncooperation without violence is a battle of the brave."

Ever more intense grew the agitation. The Prince of Wales took ship for India in November. Fearful of disorders, the government began acts of suppression. First, it declared the Congress Volunteer Corps an illegal organization. That paved the way to the arrest of members. Immediately the Volunteers announced that they would continue their work and even printed a list of members. In city after city bonfires of foreign cloth were blazing. Men tossed to the flames their fine English suits and shopkeepers contributed bolts of chiffon.

Then arrests began. In Bengal and central India police cars were busy night and day carrying Volunteers to jail. Men were arrested by the thousand. They went off waving and cheering, as if to a fair. On November 17th, Prince Edward landed at Bombay near the lofty marble arch called the Portal to India.

Gandhi was in the city that day. For a few hours he believed the boycott was going to be peaceful. Loyal Indians went to greet the royal visitor in sufficient numbers to keep the gaily decorated boulevards along the sea from looking completely deserted. Yet noncooperators did not molest them. Suddenly, however, passions blazed out. The rough element of Bombay, backed by mill workers, started a riot. Soon religious and political hatreds fanned the flames. The narrow streets between tall tenements seethed with furious battles. Property was destroyed. Numbers were killed and panic seized many sections of the city.

Gandhi risked his life by rushing to the scene to stop the rioting. Between his efforts and the stern measures of the police, order was finally restored. Next day every newspaper carried Gandhi's statement of bitter regret that an innocent plan of boycott should have been ruined by crime. "Every man has the right to his own religion and his own political opinion. Noncooperation will never succeed until men understand that."

In other places, however, such turbulence was rare. The boycott was observed with impressive dignity. As the unfortunate Prince of Wales proceeded to city after city, he was escorted through empty streets. Shops were closed and people remained at home behind drawn curtains. For this genial young man, used to popular adulation in England, Canada, New Zealand, and Australia, the trip through India must have been a cruel experience. In Calcutta the demonstration of silence was so complete that the British seemed to be ruling in a vacuum.

Infuriated editors of English papers throughout India declared that the country was being run by the Congress Volunteers. They called upon the government to act. Immediately arrests were redoubled. Now important leaders were seized. Gandhi received a telegram informing him that both Motilal and Jawaharlal Nehru had been sentenced to jail for six months. It was hard for him to think of Motilal in a prison cell. Yet the determined courage of leaders everywhere was thrilling.

Never was a session of congress so inspiring as the one held that December. An intoxicating sense of power and success possessed the members. They declared themselves ready to suffer any penalty until home rule was granted. Young men were urged to replace imprisoned members of the Volunteer Corps. Finally mass civil disobedience was demanded, and by unanimous vote Gandhi was chosen to carry out the resolution as "sole executive authority of congress."

As applause and cheers stormed up to him, Gandhi listened with a sinking heart. He walked from the platform with the dignified elderly Mohammedan who had presided over the session. "This measure is a mistake," Gandhi said to him anxiously. "Such a general order is sure to excite people to outbreaks. I'm not willing to issue it."

Gravely the older man replied, "Yes, only a small proportion of congress accepts nonviolence as a moral principle. Most of our members regard it as strategy and have no firm hold upon this new means of combat."

At the Ashram, Gandhi went into retirement to review the situation. For a time it looked as if a conference with the viceroy might be possible, but it fell through. Meanwhile, a group of farmers in the South staged a strike without consulting anybody. They refused to pay their taxes. Aggressive congress members applauded the farmers and wanted the strike to spread. But Gandhi knew that in that event the Congress Party would lose the support of every landowner in the country, for they would be bankrupt. He wired the farmers to pay their taxes at once.

Day after day the troubled leader was bombarded with telegrams and letters demanding action. At last he agreed to try mass civil disobedience in one district near Bombay. As usual he wrote a warning to the viceroy and begged him to restore to the people their liberties. Receiving no reply, he drew up final plans for the demonstration. The whole country waited breathlessly.

At an early hour on the day when he was to give the signal, Mohandas was handed a telegram. The district leaders who were with him saw the look of foreboding with which he read the message. Shuddering from head to foot, he gasped, "The worst has happened!"

Violence! In a village not very far from Allahabad a riot had taken place. Maddened people had murdered several policemen who had stopped a peaceful procession. Then they burned down police headquarters and in the building several other policemen were burned alive.

In shocked silence the district workers heard the news. "I shall wire the Congress Working Committee to meet me here at once," said Gandhi. "In the face of such an outrage I cannot start an experiment in civil disobedience."

A few days later millions of Indians, the British government, and the waiting world learned the decision of Mohandas Gandhi. It was complete abolition of active resistance. There were to be no demonstrations of mass civil disobedience—no processions and meetings of the Volunteers, no picketing, no action which would court arrest.

The country was stunned. The Indian people had stood on the very verge of success in forcing England to grant their demands. Now they were told to stop their nationwide movement. From the Nehrus and other leaders in prison, from congress members so recently triumphant, from students and other young men in every corner of India came angry and agonized protests. From the British came a tremendous sigh of relief. The revolution was ended. English prestige and vast investments were safe.

Few understood Gandhi's decision. Those who called him the Mahatma did not quite realize all that the name implied. He had staked his honor and the future of his people upon nonviolence. No political advantage, no success for superb strategy could force him to sacrifice principle. He was certain that no permanent good could be won by Indians until they had learned the law of love and sacrifice.

What he urged upon them was a program of preparation for self-government. It consisted of the development of schools and colleges supported entirely by native money and talent, a peaceful temperance campaign, spinning and weaving so that the population might be clad in *khadi*, a true effort by Hindus to "purge themselves of the sin of Untouchability."

No one could deny the importance of such activities. But where was their dramatic appeal? Men who had been organizing peasants, speaking at mammoth meetings, writing defiant articles, risking fortune and comforts in the cause of liberty, were now asked to sit down quietly and spin. A wave of depression rolled over the country. "Why punish everyone for the sins of one little group?" asked angry leaders.

Gandhi's answer fell on unheeding ears. "We dare not enter the kingdom of liberty with mere lip homage to truth and nonviolence."

One month after civil disobedience was abandoned, the British took the action they had not dared attempt before.

Already some thirty thousand Volunteers were in prison. Now with all opposition paralyzed, the viceroy knew it was safe to arrest their leader. One day officers of the law appeared at the Ashram with a warrant for Gandhi's arrest.

He had publicly warned his followers that this might happen. Without protest he went quietly off with the police. But his going shocked the colony. Weavers left their looms, teachers their classes, and gardeners their spading.

Mahadev Desai told them to accept the Mahatma's going with resignation. "Humiliation, anxiety, and sorrow have been his lot for weeks," said Desai. "Criticism from friends and co-workers has cut him to the quick. Now he is apart from the turmoil."

Gandhi was writing busily in his cell one afternoon a few days later when his door was suddenly unlocked. A guard ushered in a slender young man dressed in white *khadi*. For an instant the prisoner's eyes blinked in amazement. Before him stood Jawaharlal Nehru. The young man had felt more bitterly than almost anyone else the prostration to which Gandhi had doomed the country. Yet here he was, and his whole being radiated the same old affection.

"You are free again!" With a look of unutterable joy, Gandhi sprang up.

"Yes, Gandhiji. For some unknown reason my sentence was blotted out. But when I see you here and think of my father still in jail I am not too happy to be free."

"And your mother? Is she deeply disturbed?"

"Ah, that saint!" sighed Nehru. "She is courage itself. She sent you her warmest greetings. Tell me, Gandhiji, do you think you will be sentenced for a long term?"

Gandhi nodded. "I am accused of writing seditious pieces for *Young India* and other journals." He laughed. "And of course they were just that from a British standpoint. For less offense than mine many a fine English gentleman in times past languished for years in London Tower."

Learning by another question that Gandhi's trial was to be held in the circuit court of Ahmedabad on March 18th, Jawaharlal said almost reverentially, "I shall be there."

So he was. Standing by the door of the courtroom, the Gandhi cap perched defiantly on his head, he watched the prisoner take his place at the bar. Many Indian notables, including the general secretary of the congress, crowded the room. Outside the building hundreds of people silently waited. This hushed attention to the trial was the mood of all India.

After the prosecutor had read his stern charge placing responsibility on Gandhi for a general disloyalty, the judge asked the prisoner how he wished to plead. High and clear rang out the answer, "I plead guilty to the charges."

Then came the moment which his followers awaited. Gandhi was allowed to read a statement. Quietly, but with mighty conviction, he traced the acts of the British government which had changed him from an actively loyal worker for the empire to the organizer of noncooperation.

"I hold it to be a virtue," said he, and fire gleamed in his eyes, "to be disaffected toward a government which has done more harm to India than any previous system. India is less manly under British rule than she ever was before. I consider it to be a sin to have affection for the system."

Gravely the judge listened to this arraignment. Then in a tone of the utmost mildness he said he was not there to pass sentence on a man known by all to be of noble character and saintly life, only upon an avowed enemy of the government. He announced the sentence as six years of imprisonment without hard labor. After a pause he added, "If the course of events should make it possible for the government to reduce this period and release you, no one will be better pleased than I."

Gandhi thanked the judge for his courtesy. Turning to the general secretary of the congress, he gave this message to the country: "That the heavenly peace now reigning throughout the land shall continue is my great wish."

The judge left the courtroom. The prisoner turned to follow between his guards. But he was halted by a swift movement from the people nearest to him. They had flung themselves down before the Mahatma. Gently Gandhi made his way between figures prostrate at his feet. The inner door closed upon the slight figure, and a silence like a moment of prayer held the crowd spellbound.

Nehru laid his hand on the arm of the congressional secretary. "As long as we live," he murmured, "none of us will ever forget this occasion nor the words spoken in this place."

In a few days Gandhi was moved to a big prison not far from Poona near the west coast. Persuading the superintendent to let him have his *charka* in the cell, he settled down to a regime of spinning, meditation, and study. Once a month he was permitted to write one of his gay and spirited letters. Once a month he could receive a visitor. Only in a general way was he able to follow national events.

Discouragement was shown by the people in a dozen ways during the next years. Students began to drift back to government schools. Signs of disunity between Hindus and Mohammedans increased. With all important leaders in jail, the government tightened its hold on every district. Motilal Nehru had completed his sentence and was at work with the congress once more. But Jawaharlal had been rearrested and sentenced to nearly two years of imprisonment.

Gandhi took this news with the perspective gained by constant meditation. He was glad that spinning and weaving were going on apace, that a number of native schools were being started, and that boycotting of foreign cloth continued. He saw that India was going through a period of preparation for self-government just as he had wished.

One December day in 1923 the prison superintendent made one of his frequent calls on Gandhi. As he entered the little cell, he looked about in great alarm. The *charka* stood idle in the corner. Stretched on his cot, the prisoner lay with face drawn in pain.

"You are ill, Mr. Gandhi!" cried the superintendent. "I'll send our doctor to you at once."

Gandhi was very ill. He had appendicitis and an operation was essential. But would he consent to surgery? Everyone knew he would far rather gamble on one of his nature cures. Telegrams flew back and forth from prison officials to high authorities. What if he should die? Indians would

blame the government and ferment would result. Mohandas well knew what the prison officials feared and would
not take advantage of them. Graciously he gave his consent to the removal of his appendix.

Hardly were the words out of his mouth, when he was
whisked off to a prison hospital near Poona. Doctors,
nurses, and orderlies hung over the patient. Reports were
telephoned continually to the viceroy. For, with a fervor
equal to that of their subjects, the British hoped this arch-
rebel would survive. The operation was successful. Then
recovery was assured by the devotion lavished by the hospital staff upon the patient they had come to love.

In February, 1924, a few visitors were allowed to see
Gandhi at the prison hospital. Kasturbai, his sons, his secretary and, at last, Motilal Nehru. With a mutual respect
and affection too strong to be wrecked by political differences, the two met with open arms.

"Gandhiji!" cried Nehru. "We have all been numb with
anxiety."

To the relief of the entire country Gandhi was given his
freedom as soon as he was able to leave the hospital. In the
spring at a seaside resort his convalescence was hastened by
the presence of the entire Nehru family. Frankly they all
faced the fact that the struggle to win self-government for
India had to begin all over again.

Gandhi started at the very foundations. First of all he
tried to stop the outbreaks of murderous antagonism between Hindus and Mohammedans. They were undermin-
ing all his efforts for unity. Finding that he was making no
headway, he undertook a fast of twenty-one days, known

from then on as the Great Fast. He was at that time the
guest of a distinguished Mohammedan patriot in Delhi
and on his veranda Gandhi lay wasting away. Every few
days he either wrote or dictated a statement for the press.
He explained that he was fasting as a religious exercise of
penance and as a means of seeking the light. His host and
Mr. C. F. Andrews, who hovered over him in great anxiety,
received visitors and reporters.

Hardly had the fast begun when Mr. Andrews told
Gandhi that a peace gathering of Hindu and Mohammedan religious leaders was opening sessions in Delhi.
"They call it a unity conference, Gandhiji," said he, "so
perhaps your sacrifice will not be in vain."

"Thank you," murmured Gandhi with a smile. "I hope
between us all we shall find the remedy for this terrible
evil of religious prejudice."

Gandhi survived the long ordeal of the Great Fast.
When he was strong enough, he undertook another type of
basic reconstruction. Education, in his opinion, had been
stressing far too much the training of intellect. He wanted
schools founded by Indians to develop the whole individual. On the edge of Ahmedabad he founded a college to
serve as a model. There both professors and students had to
spend part of each day at carpentry, spinning, and manual
work.

"Indian students must not always have their noses in
books," he told educators. "They must learn the practical
skills on which daily life depends."

Nobody could deny that Gandhi himself had set the example of mastering basic skills. Chapter by chapter, in one
of the Indian papers, he was publishing his autobiography,

which is now world famous. Everyone was reading it and discovering with surprise that the Mahatma had learned to cook, to do excellent laundry work, and even to cut hair. All the new native schools included in their courses of study various kinds of hand industry.

During this period Gandhi traveled all over India. In the far northwest he made a powerful friend. This was Abdul Gaffir Khan, the Mohammedan leader of the mighty Pathan people living on the border of Afghanistan. Long ago the Pathans had heard the tale of how the forgiving leader of Indians in South Africa had defended the Pathan who attacked him in Johannesburg. These warlike giants were therefore very ready to listen to Gandhi's talks on nonviolence.

After the first meeting, the enormously tall, muscular Abdul Gaffir Khan spent two hours in talk with the tiny preacher of peace and self-sacrifice. "I shall form a group here of my people, Mahatma Gandhi," said he. "We are fighters. We will help in this battle for bloodless victory."

So eager was the Pathan chief for instruction that many times Gandhi had to make the long, wearisome journey to the Frontier Province. But he never shrank from endless trips in crowded third-class carriages. On his hundreds of visits to different villages, friends usually started him off in motor cars. But he went on by foot. When the peasants saw him coming down a village street, slightly stooped and leaning on his cane, they knelt in the dust to greet him.

"Thus did Lord Krishna visit his people. Thus did Lord Buddha walk among the poor," they would say.

Wherever he went, news of his coming ran before. In a single day he would find ten thousand people gathered in one village, twenty-five thousand at another, and at the place of the main meeting even one hundred thousand might have collected. Jawaharlal Nehru, who joined Gandhi's tour of central India, would say to him, "Bapu, these crowds seem to spring out of the ground."

Young Nehru was now the acknowledged leader of all the more aggressive members of the congress. For several years he had served as general secretary and had proved himself both brilliant and completely devoted to India's cause. Gandhi was well aware that Jawaharlal and his group were impatient with what seemed to them the total lack of progress toward the goal of independence. Yet no one admired their spirit more. He was almost sorry to join Jawaharlal's father in curbing a fiery resolution proposed by the radicals at the 1928 meeting of the congress. All the youthful members wanted to demand India's complete independence at once. But Motilal Nehru, Gandhi, and the other moderates offered the government a year in which to draft a constitution.

Even this seemed impertinent to the British. They proceeded to arrest many labor leaders and provincial organizers. Students who tried to raise funds for political prisoners were beaten by police. At a large but peaceful demonstration in one city, Jawaharlal was twice severely clubbed by mounted police who charged the marchers.

Such methods were just the right ones to inspire once more a vigorous spirit of rebellion. A common sight in many cities was a procession behind banners bearing the slogan "Long Live the Revolution." Gandhi, who did not approve of such agitation, nevertheless thought the time had come for the more belligerent members of congress to take the lead. He insisted that Jawaharlal Nehru be nominated for president at the session in December, 1929.

Just before that meeting the viceroy summoned a conference of leaders. He had made the announcement that in due course of time India would certainly be given dominion status similar to that of Canada. But at the conference he bristled when Gandhi and Motilal Nehru asked him for immediate reforms and an immediate plan for framing the constitution.

"Gentlemen," said the viceroy reprovingly, "I have no power to promise such things."

Every member of congress received a report of this conference. Every member realized that England was still only making meaningless gestures. A new determination to force the government to act filled each man. As Jawaharlal Nehru took office as president, he received a tremendous ovation. He and his committee had prepared a Declaration of Independence. The reading of it brought cheers which fairly rocked the walls. After its adoption, the congress swiftly passed a resolution that a campaign of civil disobedience was to be organized by the Working Committee.

Then occurred a dramatic episode. Suddenly on the platform the flag of Indian independence was unfurled.

In the midst of the furore greeting those horizontal stripes of saffron, green, and white, Motilal Nehru turned proudly to Gandhi. "These young men will carry that banner to victory!" he cried.

Such was the spirit which directed the great historic drama of the year 1930.

CHAPTER XII

January 26th, 1930, was chosen as india's first independence Day. Congress members read the Declaration of Independence to villagers in every part of the land. Practically the entire population held meetings at which solemn vows of loyalty were taken. It was announced that a program of civil disobedience was soon to be led by Mahatma Gandhi.

In February, Jawaharlal Nehru and Mohandas sat in the little hut at the Ashram discussing the plan. "It is certain, Gandhiji," said Nehru eagerly, "that the whole country knows now that you mean what you say—if police are resisted, disobedience will be halted. People are far more disciplined and serious than ever before. True, a few terrorists have caused trouble. But you have taught the masses that we can only win by nonviolence."

This admission by the fiery political leader touched Gandhi deeply. Yet he foresaw that Nehru would bitterly disapprove of the mild terms he finally suggested for civil disobedience. Payment of the salt tax was to be refused. That was all.

Radical congress members did recognize that this tax on an absolute necessity struck at rich and poor alike. Salt was

222

a British monopoly which earned huge revenues for the government. But the leaders said in despair, "After almost ten years of inaction, Gandhi proposes a passive course. It's no way to launch a national struggle."

Unshaken by the contempt of his co-workers, Gandhi wrote his usual warning to the viceroy. Receiving no reply, he published the letter and announced his program. He himself would start the campaign by leading a group from the Ashram to the coast. There, "from the ocean created by God," he would scoop up a handful of salt made "contraband by the British."

So immediate was the popular enthusiasm and excitement that Nehru and his aggressive party suddenly realized that Gandhi's plan was that of a genius. He was dramatizing the peaceful demand for human rights in a simple direct way that fired the imagination of everyone.

At daybreak on March 11th, Gandhi's party started from the Ashram. A number of students from the college at Ahmedabad joined the group. With his arm around Kasturbai, Mohandas led the way.

Even before the day was over, the march became world news. At every village the pilgrims were welcomed by men and women with flowers, food, shelter, and adoration. Hundreds of peasants in one village would accompany the party to the next stopping place. There hundreds more would take their places as escort. Every day Gandhi spoke to huge gatherings. He explained why British rule should end and pled for unity of all citizens, regardless of creed or caste. And so, striding along staff in hand, amid a shower of jasmine blossoms, between lines of people kneeling for his blessing, the Mahatma advanced on his two-hundred-mile walk to the sea.

At every moment his arrest was expected. The Nehrus knew that prison was yawning for them. Already substitute leaders were prepared to carry on the work. For a farewell conference with Gandhi, Motilal and his son rushed down to a small town near the coast. After the sunset service attended by thousands, the three men sat on the ground before Gandhi's tent in quiet talk.

"Gandhiji," said Motilal, "I wish to give our big house in Allahabad to the nation as a center of the freedom movement. Do you approve of that?"

"It is a beautiful deed, my friend," replied Mohandas.

As the two visitors said good-by and climbed into their motor car, Gandhi watched them with love and admiration. No greater sacrifices than theirs had been made by any of the patriots. A short time after this visit Gandhi learned that Jawaharlal was again in jail.

On April 6th, the Salt March ended at the sea. That was the signal for *satyagraha* to begin. Already townsfolk and peasants had been experimenting with homemade methods of distilling salt from sea water. Now no one would buy salt and the boycott soon included every kind of import. In the bazaars, customers would purchase only goods made in India.

With pride in his people Gandhi read letters, telegrams, and newspaper reports describing the great meetings held everywhere. Mrs. Sarajini Naidu came down to his camp to tell of the role women were playing.

"It's a sight, Gandhiji, to watch veiled Mohammedan

women and sheltered wives and daughters of Hindus and Parsis picketing liquor stores and saloons. They distribute leaflets and collect funds. The minute one of our leaders is arrested, the women in his home town organize a day of mourning."

Best of all was the fact that crowds offered little or no resistance to police. Even when brutal clubbing was followed by pistol shots, the people did not defend themselves. One morning Mrs. Naidu and Kasturbai found Gandhi in a state of excitement over a striking example of non-violence.

"News from the Frontier Province!" he cried. "Abdul Gaffir Khan has kept the pledge in the face of savage police attacks. And what do you think happened? When British officers commanded their Indian troops to fire on a crowd of Pathans, the soldiers refused. They risked execution to spare their fellow men."

Gandhi now wrote a second letter to the viceroy to ask that, as a deed of good will, the oppressive salt tax be removed at once. He added advance notice of his next project, which was to take possession of the salt works near his camp for the benefit of the nation. A curt reply informed him that such lawlessness would be punished. Immediately Gandhi took up his march again.

One lovely May night when sea breezes blended with the dusty odor from millet fields, Gandhi slept in his tent. He did not hear a motor car sliding to a stop outside. Suddenly flashlights blazed in his face. A ring of armed police surrounded his bed. "You are under arrest," said a voice.

Looking quietly around, Gandhi said to the local Indian

magistrate, "Will you be good enough, sir, to read the summons?"

Before the official's quavering voice had ceased, dozens of Gandhi's followers were at the tent door. Gandhi asked permission to have them sing his favorite hymn. As the last note died away, he sprang up, wrapped his cloak about him, and jumped into the waiting police car.

"Gandhiji," called out one of the group, "haven't you a special message for Ba?"

"Tell her she is a brave girl," he replied.

Back in prison at his old regime of spinning, meditating, and writing, Mohandas was unaware of the sensation created by his arrest. It made front-page news in journals all over the Western world. England's prime minister received a cable signed by one hundred and twenty American clergymen, begging him to make peace with India. The same appeal was sent from India itself by groups of British and Indian businessmen. Trade was at a standstill. Industrial workers were on strike. Tax payments were refused. Unwanted imports clogged the shelves of stores.

At that very moment in London, parliament was holding a round-table conference on plans for an Indian constitution. Liberals wanted action, and early in 1931 Gandhi and many other leaders, including Motilal and Jawaharlal Nehru, were released from prison.

Freedom, however, came too late for Motilal. His health had failed and he was brought home only to die. Jawaharlal never left his father's side. Gandhi, who had hastened to Allahabad, gave what comfort he could to Mrs. Nehru, her daughters, and their husbands. It was Gandhi who spoke to the mighty throngs who followed the body of the great leader to the funeral pyre beside the sacred Ganges River.

Less than a month later, Gandhi was in New Delhi conferring with the viceroy on peace terms. That England had been forced to any sort of compromise thrilled even conservative Indians. The final pact was far from satisfactory. But at least all political prisoners were released and severe measures against picketers and demonstrators were withdrawn.

In early summer the British government appointed a number of titled Mohammedans and ultraconservative Hindus as delegates to the London Round Table Conference. In spite of its thousands upon thousands of members from every part of the country, the Indian Congress was permitted only one representative. To choose him, a meeting was called at Karachi on the northwest coast. Before the session began, the mammoth camp near the meeting hall buzzed with sociability. Suddenly a hullabaloo arose. A large body of men all dressed in red shirts had come marching into camp and no one knew who they were.

Then through the jumble of excited voices came a thunderous shout from the leader of the band. "Where is Mahatma Gandhi? I am Abdul Gaffir Khan and we have come from the Frontier Province to join the Congress Party."

This first appearance of the Pathans was applauded to the echo. Their leader was greeted with marked affection by Gandhi. His earnestness made such an appeal to congress members that they began calling him the Frontier Gandhi, a name taken up throughout India.

Elected unanimously as the congress delegate, Gandhi

set sail for England in late August. Nehru went to Bombay to say farewell. Sorrowing for his father, unhappy about Gandhi's peace settlement with the viceroy, doubtful about the London conference, Jawaharlal was steeped in gloom.

Mohandas tried to lighten his mood. "I shall give the English cartoonists a good time anyway," he laughed. "Aside from my costume, there is my little goat who goes with me to provide fresh milk."

In London a distinguished group of sympathizers welcomed Gandhi with a splendid reception. Writers, poets, artists, philosophers all assured him they had followed with eager hope India's brave struggle for freedom and they expressed their personal friendship.

"Mr. Gandhi," said one famous novelist, "I hear you are staying with a friend who heads a settlement house in the slums. Such consistency charms us very much. But I hope our street urchins aren't too rude to you."

"Oh, they run after me and shout my name," laughed Mohandas, "and even jeer a bit, but I'll win them over in time."

So he did. Soon the youngsters waited for him at the settlement house door, calling him Uncle Gandhi. One evening, hearing that he had been to a garden party at Buckingham Palace, they came shouting, "Uncle Gandhi, did you really see the king?"

"Yes, indeed," he said, smiling, "and I thought him a very pleasant gentleman."

One of his Indian friends, with a glance at Gandhi's costume, asked him if he had appeared at the party just like that. "I did," he replied. "You see, His Majesty wore enough clothes for two."

Any chance for laughter was precious to Mohandas during those grim weeks at the Round Table Conference. The constitution framed by the British was designed to keep India in subjection to the empire. It extended the vote and gave elected officers more power, but as a means of creating self-government for a free people the plan was a farce.

With brilliant clearness Gandhi spoke on all the points discussed—finance, trade, election systems, control of the army, and the high courts of law. His plea for the main issue, independence for India, impressed neither parliament members nor the pro-British Indians at the Round Table. At the end of the session, weary and discouraged, he took ship for home.

At Bombay shocking news awaited him. A new viceroy had discarded the peace pact. Arrests were continuous. The congress had been declared illegal. On his way to meet Gandhi, Nehru had been seized and sentenced to two years of imprisonment. Bengal and central India were torn by disorders.

Heartsick, Gandhi asked for an interview with the viceroy. The answer was an order to arrest Gandhi and also the president of congress. Kasturbai, Mrs. Naidu, and several other followers of Gandhi were arrested shortly afterwards. Among the hundreds of women sentenced to prison were Nehru's lovely delicate wife, his two sisters, and even his courageous old mother.

Although 1932 saw the complete triumph of force, Gandhi undertook from prison one act of resistance. In London he had insisted that Untouchables be treated like other citizens. Suddenly he learned that the Indians chosen by the British to work on the constitution had agreed that there should be entirely separate elections for Untouchables.

To the friend who brought the news Mohandas cried out, "Separate treatment of Untouchables cannot be allowed! Here is an attempt to make Untouchability last forever!" Springing up from his seat beside the *charka*, he said in a tone of desperation, "Unless Untouchability is destroyed, we can never have sound self-government!"

"But, Gandhiji," exclaimed his friend, aghast at the impassioned outburst, "what can you do about this election law?"

"I can die!" was the prompt answer. "I shall resist this wicked provision with my life!"

Before the day was over he had written the English prime minister that unless the election plan was changed, he meant to fast unto death. Public announcement of this intention threw the country into panic. A conference of all the Indian notables at work on the constitution was called at Bombay. Telegrams begging Gandhi not to risk death flooded his cell.

To all he answered, "My religious conviction as a Hindu bids me give my life if necessary to make up for the terrible wrongs done by Hindus to helpless men and women." At noon on September 20th the fast began.

The prisoner's cot was moved into the tiny yard outside his cell under a huge mango tree. Each day the visiting doctor reported his condition and the news was flashed around the world. On the fourth day of the fast a new plan for elections was sent by the group at Bombay, and Gandhi approved it. At once it was cabled to England's prime minister.

All prison rules had gone down before the avalanche of concern rushing toward Gandhi. Kasturbai and a group of Ashram workers spent hours beside his cot. Nehru's daughter and niece came to see him. One afternoon the tall black-robed figure of Rabindranath Tagore stooped over the wasted man under the mango tree.

"You are a dauntless warrior, Mahatma Gandhi," said Tagore, "to fight for India's most neglected group with your only weapon—your life."

Tagore was in the prison yard on September 26th when the great news came. The prime minister had accepted the changed election plan. Amid jubilation, Tagore, at Gandhi's request, sang one of his hymns and recited an ancient prayer. As the thin musical voice ceased, Gandhi broke his fast. That sip of fruit juice was an international event.

When Gandhi finished his prison term, he knew just what he wanted to do. Leaving politics to the Congress Party, he devoted himself to the two major problems of Indian life. The first of these was Untouchability. His Ashram had been seized by the government after the Salt March in 1930. The colony formed then around a little retreat of Gandhi's near Wharda in the center of India, and there the All-India Spinners Association had its headquarters. When the Sabarmati Ashram was returned to Gandhi, he devoted it to the Untouchable group. From that center radiated a nation-wide effort to stamp out this ancient evil.

Gandhi's other main interest was to inspire unity between Hindus and Mohammedans. That was not difficult in villages where the two groups had managed for years to live peaceably together. But among educated men of position, antagonism had grown greater ever since Mr. Jinnah had left the congress and devoted himself to the Moslem League. Once he had worked with Gandhi to bring the two groups together, but now he seemed deliberately to be creating a split between them. Fearful clashes occurred constantly.

Nehru had his own explanation of the change. He said to Gandhi, "Jinnah couldn't bear the middle-class congress members who swarmed by the thousands into the party. He is too elegant and too ambitious. As the all-powerful head of the Moslem League, he means to make it our strong rival."

The first test of Jinnah's strength came in 1936. For then the so-called constitution was forced upon the Indian people and elections were held in those provinces not governed by native princes. The Moslem League won in only three of them and the congress won in eight.

Gandhi wrote to congratulate Nehru on the results of the election. Jawaharlal's sister, Mrs. Pandit, was one of the eight executives chosen as a result of the election. But Gandhi knew that Nehru was as unhappy as were most thoughtful Indians about the new government. For with real controls in the hands of the British, even the provincial ministers had no power.

Gandhi was often troubled about Jawaharlal. Without deep religious feeling, the young man had little relief from suffering. Long years in prison, the death of his wife, the unsuccessful struggle for India's freedom had darkened his outlook. Now he was more sharply aware than most of his fellow workers how deadly serious was the situation in Europe. For these were the years when Adolf Hitler was rising to power in Germany. Backed as he was by vast and frightful armaments and by huge bodies of trained troops, the Nazi chief had begun to feel himself invincible.

To Gandhi something else was almost as appalling as the threat from such mad ambition. This was the passive terror of the other countries. They were all bargaining with Hitler for safety. No courage, no unity between European nations, no daring moral force opposed the tyrant. With Nehru's certainty that war was inevitable Gandhi completely agreed. The horror of it stood starkly before him. Yet he could experience joy from spiritual sources and was always as ready to laugh as a bird is to sing.

Strangers visiting the Ashram for the first time and prepared to meet a saint were often startled by his teasing ways. An American woman, long a worker for peace, appeared at his hut one day for a scheduled interview. According to the custom of the place she slipped off her muddy shoes and started across the veranda. She was amazed to hear Gandhi's laughing voice call out from indoors, "I see, madam, you need to practice walking in stocking feet."

Later, during their serious discussion, he said, "Even in this black moment of doom let's not forget that laughter is healing."

At last Hitler, having snapped his fingers at all treaties and broken every promise to the governments which tried to appease him, ordered his army into Poland. Then England and France had to act. On September 3rd, 1939, they declared war on Nazi Germany and the Second World War began.

Eleven days later the British government gave Indian leaders a rude shock. The viceroy made an announcement as autocratic as that of any czar. He declared that the people of India were to give active support to England in the struggle against Germany. Not a single conference had he held with Indians in high position. With no warning whatsoever the country was made responsible for war effort.

Immediately Gandhi was flooded with telegrams asking his advice. His answer was in keeping with his belief in nonviolence. "Remember that England is involved in a fight for life. Let us take no advantage of her."

It was with his approval, however, that congress leaders sent the viceroy a challenge. If this was truly a war for democracy and freedom, then England should cease autocratic rule in India. To arouse united effort in the country, the government should make an immediate declaration of India's independence and urge the election of a special assembly to frame a constitution of government for all the people. That was the message from patriots.

The answer was no. What England wanted was volunteers as well as drafted men for the army, munition factories, and money. What the government meant to keep was absolute control.

Immediately the ministers in all the provinces resigned. Then the British governors of the provinces suspended the assemblies. The land was ruled by edicts from the viceroy and his aides. Acting on the good will and restraint taught by Gandhi, leaders took no action. But faced by the collapse of Norway, Holland, Belgium, and France, in the spring of 1940 Indian patriots tried to find some honorable means of opposing Fascism.

Again and again a group met at the Wharda Ashram. Seated on the spotless floor of Gandhi's little room, shaded by rose and bougainvillaea vines, they talked of their longing for action. Finally the experienced leader from Madras came forward with a new proposal. This was to set up an All-India provisional government which would work with the British authorities and unite the country for defense.

"It is a perfectly practical idea," argued Nehru eagerly.

With this Gandhi agreed. But in his lack of enthusiasm the others found a fear that such a government would involve the land in war.

Yet when this proposal was refused by the British, Gandhi was indignant. He was as shocked as Nehru by the pronouncements of the viceroy. It was plain that even after the war the British Empire would not accept an Indian government for and by the whole people. Therefore Gandhi agreed to attend a meeting of the All-India Congress Committee to decide what to do next. It was held one October day in 1940 in a suburb of Bombay. The meeting hall was packed and a vast throng gathered outside.

High-school and college students, carrying the Indian Independence flag, lined a pathway through the mass of people to the door. As Nehru and Gandhi stepped out of a motor car, the crowd went wild. "Victory!" they shouted. "Gandhi Kai-jai!" "Jai! Jai! Mahatma!"

As the two leaders entered the hall, a roar of applause went up from the people on the floor and in the galleries.

Scarcely looking at them, Gandhi quietly seated himself on the bare planks of the platform beside the *charka* placed there for him and began to spin.

At that meeting it was decided to protest England's utter indifference to the hopes of a vast population. Civil disobedience was to be undertaken. But in order not to dislocate England's desperate struggle against Germany, only individuals and not mass groups would be involved. One by one leaders would hold forbidden meetings or speak against British imperialism.

"This will mean imprisonment, of course," said Gandhi and added with a smile for the audience, "but we've all been in prison before."

Nehru was arrested one week later. Month by month other arrests followed until some thirty thousand Congress Party members were in prison. Gandhi devoted his liberty to the cause of brotherhood and nonviolence. His was the only great voice in the world declaring absolute faith in moral and spiritual force.

One evening at his prayer meeting before an audience which stretched out like the sea, he said, "We have to make truth and nonviolence not matters for mere individual practice but for practice by groups, communities, and nations. That, at any rate, is my dream. I shall live and die trying to realize it."

He was a lonely dreamer during the next year. Hitler dominated the war on sea and land and in the air. Japan, Germany's ally, was moving against Singapore. Then suddenly his loneliness ended. Nehru and many other political prisoners were freed. They left prison in early December,

1941, just three days before Japan struck both at Pearl Harbor and at English posts in the Far East.

Nehru was welcomed back to freedom by Gandhi like a long-lost son. Together they talked over the bewildering problems facing their country. "Our people have sunk down into sullen submission," said Nehru. "Even fighting is better than that."

When Japan conquered Burma and threatened India on the one hand and China on the other, inaction became intolerable. Even Gandhi began to feel that his pacifism might stand in the way of India's future position among the nations fighting for freedom. Therefore, from a sense of patriotic duty he came out strongly for the provisional government and stated that a free India could throw great resources into the struggle against aggressors. His articles and speeches excited the people and once more the intense longing for action surged through the land.

On August 8th, 1942, a meeting of the All-India Congress Committee was held. Solemnly they added up the score against the British government of India which had degraded and enfeebled the country. The provisional government was once more proposed with enthusiasm.

When Gandhi rose to speak, all the emotional stress he had experienced in the last three years rose to the surface. "We can no longer hold back our people from exercising their will. Nor can we go on eternally submitting to imperialist authority. The time has come for the English to go. Civil servants, army officers, government officials—all of them should quit India."

It was some time before the cheering stopped. But before

the meeting ended, a long resolution, known ever after as
the Quit India Bill, was drawn up for presentation to the
government.

That government, however, was not asleep. Before dawn
its police were busy. Not only in Bombay but all over the
country, hundreds of arrests were made. At six in the morning policemen came to arrest Gandhi and Mahadev Desai.
Although the telephone wires into the house had been cut
to assure secrecy, the people were somehow warned and
crowds stood in the street shouting "Gandhi—Kai-jai!"

This time Gandhi's jail had more than a touch of lux-
ury. It was the splendid palace of the great Aga Khan in
Bombay, which the English had taken over. With one of
those kindly gestures for which the British are famous,
Gandhi was surrounded by a choice group of prisoners.
Kasturbai was transferred to the palace with her doctor, a
young woman just graduating from medical school. Mrs.
Naidu came to bring cheer and devoted friendliness. Another friend was a young Englishwoman, daughter of Ad-
miral Slade. Miraben, as her Indian friends called her, had
been living at the Ashram for years. She was in charge of
the weaving and also acted as Gandhi's secretary. The prisoners could walk in the pleasant garden and had servants
to wait upon them. Yet the palace was a prison for all that.
Not only was it hard to be out of touch with the tremendous events of the war, but it was also painful to sit helpless
before India's crying need. Stories of a terrible famine in
Bengal darkened the days.

From the news that trickled into the Aga Khan palace
during the next eighteen months it was plain that the Allies

would ultimately win. The United States had flung her full power into the war. The Soviet Union, after defeating the German army at Stalingrad, began to roll it back. In the Far East, Japan was definitely checked.

The dawn of 1944, however, found India enduring bitter trials. Nearly a million people had died of famine. All the strong leaders were in prison. Others—Rabindranath Tagore, Mr. C. F. Andrews, Mahadev Desai—were dead. In February of that year another bereavement brought general mourning.

One afternoon a strange scene took place in the courtyard of the Aga Khan palace. A still small figure covered with flowers lay on a funeral pyre of sandalwood. Kneeling beside it were a group of prisoners and three of Gandhi's sons. Seated against the wall with eyes closed in prayer, Mohandas Gandhi was taking silent farewell of the selfless companion whose devotion had enfolded him for sixty years. Kasturbai had died in prison.

Doubtless his grief was part of the reason that Gandhi's health began to fail. His anemia and weakness frightened the British and he was released in May. This was just a month before D-Day, the stupendous attack by the Allies on German forces massed on the west coast of France. Before the end of the year Gandhi foresaw that Fascism would be defeated and he began to discuss with other leaders plans for a people's government. They were certain that after the war British resistance to their will to freedom would crumble.

As soon as he had recovered strength, Gandhi began rebuilding dykes of good will. Religious antagonism was now threatening to overwhelm the country. For several years M. A. Jinnah had been setting forth a demand which seemed preposterous even to thousands of Mohammedans. He wanted a section carved out of India as a separate Mohammedan country with its own government. Recently he had named it Pakistan. To Gandhi the idea of such division was a nightmare. He finally persuaded Jinnah to confer with him.

The tall, thin gentleman in English clothes, with a monocle in one eye, looked coldly down at his visitor. He listened with a superior smile as Gandhi said that Indian feuds gave England a perfect excuse for continuing her controls.

"I have always worked for India's self-government," replied Jinnah haughtily. "It will come, and with it the right of Mohammedans to have a separate nationality."

At this Gandhi cried out, "Cut me in two if you will, but do not cut India in two!" But he spoke to deaf ears.

On May 4th, 1945, the German armies surrendered to
the Allies. By that time the defeat of Japan by the United
States was also certain. Five months later an election was
held in England and reports of its results flashed hope of
speedy action throughout India.

The news was told Gandhi by his trusted helper, Miraben. The Englishwoman's face was alight as she said,
"Bapu, the British war government has fallen and the
Labor Party was elected to power. Surely now this land will
win its freedom."

At first, however, the Labor government seemed as cau-
tious about giving up power in India as its predecessor. But
at least the prisons were emptied of political agitators and
consent was given to the election of an assembly to frame
India's first really democratic constitution. Nehru and many
others believed that if members of the Moslem League
worked with the Congress Party to form a new government,
they might drop the idea of Pakistan.

For his part Gandhi tried to bridge the terrible gap in a
personal way. Up and down the land he traveled, pouring
out eloquent pleas for an indivisible nation. As usual, thousands of people came to hear and reverence the Mahatma.
But hate and suspicion had been unleashed. When the Mohammedan group withdrew from the constitutional assembly, the Hindus were wild with fury. Their newspapers
printed savage attacks on Jinnah and the League. A radical
Hindu society was formed to combat Pakistan by all and
any means. Naturally such bitter dissension among men
of education was reflected in violence among the masses.
In the towns of Bengal, Bihar, and the Punjab, street fight-

ing was continuous. Calcutta became a bloody battle-
ground. By the beginning of 1947 some twelve thousand
people had been killed in riots.

It was a period of anguish for Gandhi. To those who
came to him for comfort he could only say, "Let us hope
that this shameful violence will prove no more than a para-
graph in the glorious new chapter of Indian history."

He was grateful that the British government had at last
announced its withdrawal from the country. In January,
1947, amid general jubilation, India was proclaimed an
independent sovereign republic. In March, Lord Mountbatten arrived as the last viceroy, whose only task was to
wind up British affairs.

Gandhi was one of the first to welcome him, and at once
he became friendly with the young and lovely Lady Mountbatten. Over the teacups at the palace she asked, "Mr.
Gandhi, have you agreed yet to Mr. Jinnah's demand for
a separate nation?"

At that time he uttered a firm no. But during the next
weeks he saw that the Moslem League would never accept
the terms of Lord Mountbatten's final settlement unless
Pakistan became a fact. With a single blow Jinnah had cut
Gandhi's heart, as well as India, in two pieces.

One day Nehru arrived at the Wharda Ashram for a talk
with Gandhi. Even as he greeted his visitor, Mohandas
flung out the question which was haunting him night and
day. "Is there no way out? No hope of a united India?"

Nehru looked gravely at his friend. Never before had
Gandhi worn the look of age. His glowing eyes, his fresh
unwrinkled skin, and the litheness of his frail body had

always offset spectacles, baldness, and the cane on which he leaned. Now, however, the old vitality was not there. The fearful slaughter among his people had sapped it.

"Gandhiji," replied Nehru, "I am certain unity is impossible. Dreadful as is the idea of a separate country within our borders, we have to accept it. Otherwise, this deadly turmoil will never cease."

At this Gandhi bowed his head to hide his despair.

One June evening an exceptionally large crowd came to the prayer service in Gandhi's quarters in the Untouchable section of Delhi. After the songs, a passage from the sacred Koran of Mohammed was read. When the moment came for Gandhi to speak, he turned his gaze from the sunset colors of rose and gold, still glowing over the roof tops, to the upturned faces. Quietly, but with infinite sadness, he announced that he had accepted Pakistan.

A gasp rippled through the audience. Angry murmurs were heard. In a stern tone Gandhi said, "All India must accept Pakistan in loving resignation. We have no choice. Hindus must lead the way to a friendly settlement."

No one had thought that Gandhi, the great teacher of unity, would yield to Jinnah. When his decision was wired about the country, a deluge of passionate protest poured over him. Members of the radical Hindu group even vowed vengeance upon the leader. But he rose vigorously to the challenge. In speeches, articles, and interviews he repeated his theme: "No one can force belief in unity. Mohammedans are our brothers and their demands must be respected."

Whenever it was needed, Gandhi gave his counsel to the men engaged in the massive task of transferring all government departments to Indian officials. Equally difficult was settlement of the Pakistan borders. The final boundaries pleased neither party and their announcement raised mass dissension to hurricane pitch.

Yet there was one moment that summer of united triumph. Lord Mountbatten, anxious to leave a situation he could no longer control, announced the completion of his task and the departure of every British official for England. News that two hundred years of subjection to foreign rule had ended thrilled India's millions. Mammoth crowds assembled at New Delhi on August 15th, 1947, for the historic final ceremony.

Standing under the flags of India and Pakistan, the viceroy made a warm and eloquent farewell speech. In it he reminded his hearers that to no one did the country owe its independence so much as to Mahatma Gandhi.

Gandhi was not there to receive this wreath of praise. The cheers roaring up for Lord Mountbatten did not reach his ears. Alone and in silence, far from the scene of celebration, he was praying for his people and for peace.

But there was no peace. For now, throughout the whole northern section of the land, a vast upheaval of the population had begun. Millions of Hindus were leaving Bengal, the Punjab, and the Frontier Province. Millions of Mohammedan families were moving from former homes into the new state of Pakistan. In the confusion fanatics on both sides let loose their fury. Murder and destruction halted caravans on the open road and trains on their tracks. The beautiful land of Kashmir, which was still in dispute, fairly ran with blood. Calcutta would have become a charnel house had Gandhi not rushed to the city. He went straight to the home of a Mohammedan friend and this daring gesture of brotherhood shamed citizens into dropping their murderous quarrels.

Such was the exhausting effect of these horrors upon Gandhi that his friends were deeply disturbed. One of them, a wealthy industrialist named Birla, insisted that he stay in the summerhouse of his mansion at Delhi. As usual, streams of personal friends, government leaders, foreign visitors, and correspondents poured through the garden to beg for interviews. But sometimes Gandhi's devoted young nieces, who served as secretaries and guardians, refused them admission. "Bapu must be alone now," they said.

Lonely indeed was his wrestle with the forces of evil. Failure in his greatest effort weighed him down. Long before he had striven for India's independence, his work for brotherhood had begun. Yet his efforts had been in vain. Surely if he were powerful enough in spirit, he might still inspire harmony among his people! Fasting, he reflected, had always helped him to receive strength from spiritual sources. It would, moreover, be a proper penance for failing to prevent the crimes and violence shattering the land. At last he announced his decision and on January 13th, 1948, his fast began.

Gloom descended upon India. That very day the stock exchange closed. Everyone thought the Mahatma was too old and frail to survive another fast. Anxiety for his life suddenly replaced the ferocity in men's hearts. The new central government of India set an example of friendliness. For fear a certain large fund owed to Pakistan would be used to pay for a military invasion of Kashmir, it had been held in the treasury. Now the government turned the money over to the Mohammedan state.

In Delhi and in many other cities, people tried to show a similar spirit of mutual trust. Hindus and Mohammedans marched side by side in peace parades. Prayers for the Mahatma were made from coast to coast. At last a group of the strictest Hindus went to Birla House to inquire on what terms Gandhi would break his fast. He named seven conditions. Shortly after this a general peace committee of all the main religious groups presented him a pledge. Their members would be required to abide by the conditions. So it was that on January 18th, at the behest of a penitent people, Gandhi broke his fast.

Some days later he attended the evening prayer meeting. He was carried in a chair to the terrace beyond the rose garden. The occasion seemed like the beginning of peace for India. Suddenly, in the midst of the singing of the familiar hymn to Sita Ram, Great God, a sound like a muffled clap of thunder came from a hedge at the end of the garden. Through a mild commotion the singers continued and Gandhi gave no sign of noticing anything amiss.

When he had been carried back to his cot, his niece bent over him anxiously. "Bapu, a bomb exploded in the garden tonight!"

"Ah?" Mohandas sighed. "Some poor young fanatic threw it, I suppose. Don't let anybody order more guards around Birla House. This incident only means that we must redouble our efforts for mutual understanding."

On the evening of January 30th, Gandhi felt strong and

happy. He had had every indication that the pledge of peace was being kept. Wrapping about him a soft cloak of white wool, he started out for the sunset service. His two nieces walked beside him, but he did not lean upon them.

Pausing a moment, he pointed to the flower beds. "How sweet is the fragrance from those petunias," he said.

As he reached the terrace, he was conscious of a wave of loving welcome silently wafted toward him. As he smiled in response, a youth sprang forward from behind a hibiscus tree and knelt at his feet, as if seeking his blessing. Graciously Gandhi stooped toward the crouching figure.

One! Two! Three! Four! Small dull explosions thudded against the stillness. The limp body of Mohandas Gandhi sank down on the grassy terrace. The garden was deathly quiet. Voices murmured in horror, "No, no! Not the Mahatma!" People moved or stood as if in a trance. Even the young American from the United States embassy who caught the fleeing assassin did so almost in silence. As he pinioned the hands which still clutched the pistol, policemen rushed up to seize the captive. He did not struggle. No shouts of fury followed as he was led away.

Gandhi's nieces were kneeling beside him. Intently they both listened to the words which came as a mere whisper between stiffening lips. "Hai, Ram!" Gandhi murmured, speaking the name of God on his last breath.

He was gathered up and borne to his cot in the summerhouse. In the garden the crowd, urged by policemen, ebbed slowly away. But around the pavilion with its glass doors many men and women knelt, weeping silently.

It was several hours before Nehru could be notified.

When he came into the hushed room, the doctors were no longer busy with quick fingers and shining instruments. They could only shake their heads. Nehru looked down at the motionless figure lying as if in sleep upon the narrow bed. Instinctively Nehru's hand touched the thin fingers folded above the sheet. "Gandhiji!" he whispered. "Hai, Gandhiji!"

At last, turning away with a look of stunned disbelief, Nehru asked the policeman standing near by, "Who did this deed?"

Choking back a sob, the officer told the facts. A young fanatic, member of the Hindu society pledged to fight Pakistan to the bitter end, had closed forever the lips which had preached resignation and peace.

Nehru gasped, "Thank God he was not a Mohammedan!"

One of the men in the room touched Nehru's arm and said, "You will have to tell the people. You must speak to them on the radio."

Late that evening India's millions learned the tragic news. Nehru's voice trembled through the night to cities in every province.

"Friends and comrades," came the message, "the light has gone out of our lives." Asking that prayers be made, he said, "The greatest prayer is to pledge ourselves to serve the truth and the cause for which this great countryman of ours lived and for which he has died."

Next day they began to come from the far corners of the earth, those cabled tributes from kings and presidents, artists, workers, those who spent themselves for humanity's cause. Mohandas Gandhi belonged not to India alone but to the people of the world.

He had no possessions to leave except a pair of worn sandals and his spectacles. Yet no one ever bestowed such gifts. He had brought freedom to a great people and had shown humanity the path to brotherhood and peace. A merry saint, a loving warrior, Gandhi lived his adventurous life on earth as if he had been loaned from Heaven for that purpose.